CM0801257

STONE

Dedicated to my father,
to whom I owe my love of photography

This edition first published in 2005 by
New Holland Publishers (UK) Ltd
London · Cape Town · Sydney · Auckland

10 9 8 7 6 5 4 3 2 1

www.newhollandpublishers.com

Garfield House
86–88 Edgware Road
London
W2 2EA
United Kingdom

Copyright © 2005 in translation:
New Holland Publishers (UK) Ltd

ISBN 1 84537 289 1

Publishing Manager   Jo Hemmings
Senior Editor   Kate Michell
Assistant Editor   Kate Parker
Translator   Christine Shuttleworth

©   Elisabeth Sandmann Verlag GmbH, München
1st edition 2004
ISBN 3-938045-00-0
All rights reserved
Project Editor   Lily Honegger-Schaad
Editor   Eva Römer
Design, DTP   Georg Feigl, Barbara Markwitz
Production   Karin Mayer, Peter Karg-Cordes
Lithography   Detail AG, Zurich
Printing and binding   Egedsa, Sabadell

GEORG KERN

STONE

Colours and forms of a hidden world

Text by Andreas Honegger

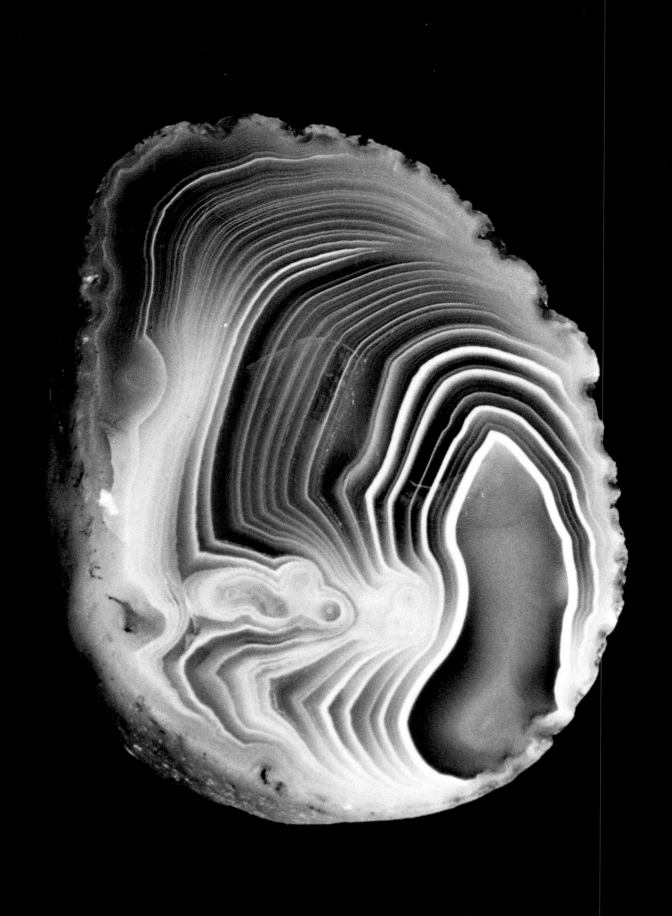

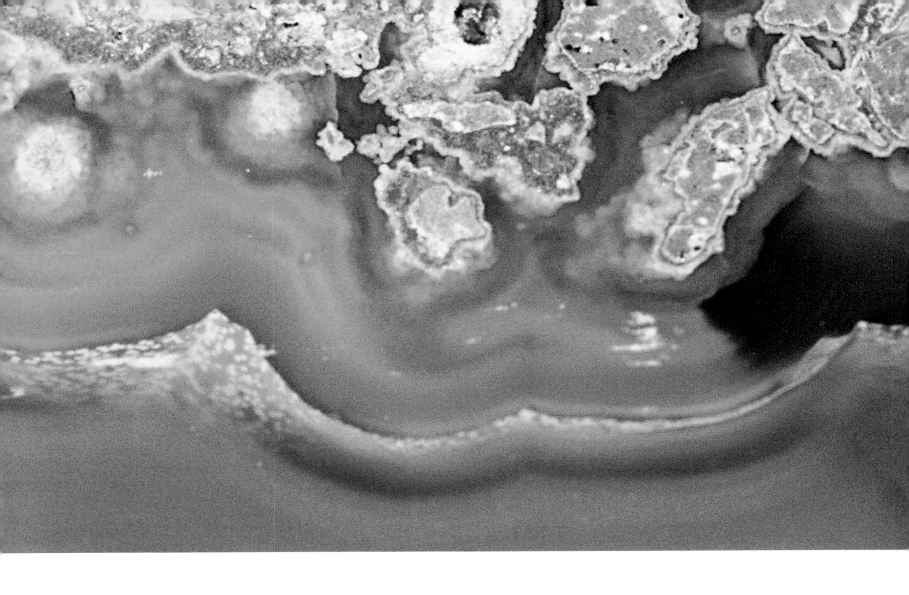

CONTENTS

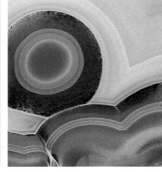
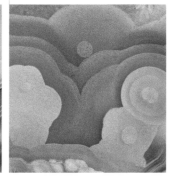
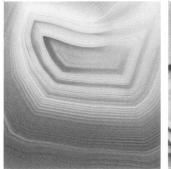

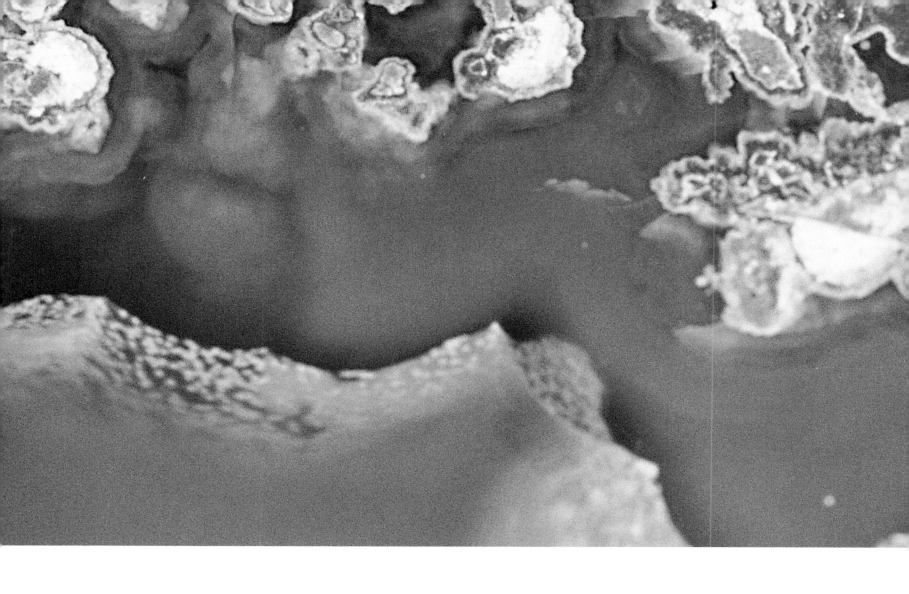

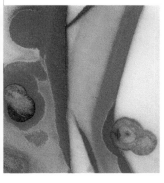

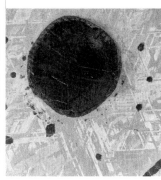
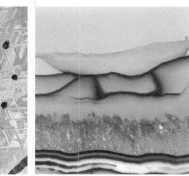

THE HIDDEN BEAUTY
WITHIN THE STONE

GEORG KERN | At work with the stereomicroscope
(Photograph: Geneviève Wohnlich-Duley)

Colours and forms in stone – there is an inescapable fascination in the beauty of minerals. Yet the splendour and diversity of this inanimate aspect of nature is hidden from most people. It is only the expert treatment of these lumps of rock, mostly so inconspicuous at first glance, that can conjure up all the subtleties of structure and colour. This treatment essentially involves sawing through the rock, and cutting and polishing its surfaces.

The wonderful world of minerals contains a limitless diversity of colours and forms. The challenge for the photographer is to find the most photogenic combinations and to select ideal subjects.

Photography has shaped my life. In the mid-1930s, when I was not yet ten years old, my parents, enthusiastic

photographers at the time, gave me my first camera – a black Kodak box. Later, my father's Leica accompanied me on my first major journeys. Travel photography has been at the centre of my interests for more than fifty years. On my countless expeditions around the world, I have been fascinated by people with their strange cultures, and by untouched and often almost inaccessible nature. I was also spellbound by works created by human hands, buildings connected with cultural history, and modern architecture.

A special and especially ambitious form of photography that I practised was underwater photography. In more than 500 diving sessions in oceans near and far, my underwater camera nearly always came with me. I was enthralled by close-ups of corals with their wonderful colours, hidden in the depths of the sea, far more so than by a massive shark filling the viewfinder.

In my long career as an ear, nose and throat specialist, I trained my eye to recognize small details, sometimes with the help of the stereomicroscope; this later stood me in good stead when photographing minerals.

For almost forty years now I have been deeply committed to the collection of minerals – admittedly, until recently concentrating on well crystallized and thus aesthetically fine pieces. The cut and polished pieces were in my collection for the sake of completeness, but led a comparatively shadowy existence there.

When I prepared an inventory of my collection and carefully inspected the agates under the stereomicroscope, I was fascinated by the beauty of their colours and forms.

The idea of recording these artworks of nature in photographs was born. Gripped by the project, I began to take photographs of some of the pieces. I took them in full sunlight with a Nikon F-100 camera, fitted with a 105-mm close-up lens and 200 Kodak ASA-negative films. To my delight and surprise, these pictures were so successful that I searched my collection for further photogenic polished stones. I soon learned to overcome the technical problem of the reflection of sunlight on the shining surfaces.

This was the beginning of a lengthy artistic learning process. Taking the important advice of an artist friend, which was decisive for me, I began to take only photographs of sections of the polished stone surface with the close-up lens. With these photographs of very small sections of the stone's surface, the person looking at the image could no longer recognize straight away that it was a stone that had been the model for the photograph. Thus images were created that are often reminiscent of abstract art, and are nevertheless a pure, unaltered depiction of nature.

At this point I would like to record the fact that my photographs have not been manipulated or retouched in any way. In addition, all have been taken in natural sunlight, without the use of any artificial light sources.

When I had photographed all the suitable pieces and sections in my collection, I went in search of new photogenic subjects. As well as new acquisitions, I was also given the opportunity to photograph special examples from a first-class private collection. This enormously increased the diversity of the minerals photographed.

After intensive photographic work over many months, I had a rich collection of highly diverse images, consisting of eighty photographs in 35 x 50 cm and 50 x 75 cm format. On 5 October, 2002 I opened my first exhibition at the Klinik Schloss Mammern on Lake Constance. To my surprise, it was a huge success with the press and public.

The great number of mineral images at my disposal inspired the wish to create an illustrated volume. This book does not claim to be a textbook on mineralogy, rather my hope is that it will convey my pleasure and delight in looking at these artworks of nature, and awaken these too for those who see and read.

My sincere thanks to the following persons:

My wife Marianne Kern, who gave her full support to my great photographic project and helped me with the selection of images; Lily Honegger-Schaad, for her artistic choice of images as well as the great administrative tasks that she undertook as project manager for my exhibitions and the publication of this book; Dr Andreas Honegger, journalist at the *Neue Zürcher Zeitung*, mineral lover and collector, for his text; and Hansjakob Siber, the great mineral expert, for kindly permitting me to photograph minerals from his private collection.

Dr Georg Kern

THE MACROCOSM AND THE POLISHED MINERAL

The world of stones in a world made of stones

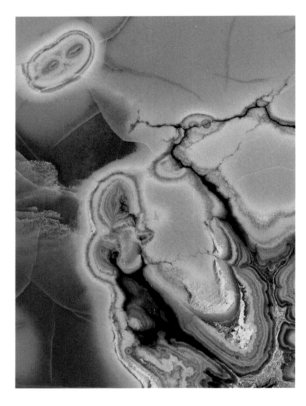

VARISCITE | FAIRFIELD, UTAH, USA

Our planet is a heavenly body made of minerals; the Earth consists of the waters of the oceans and the rocky plates that form the continents. It was from the interplay of water and slowly eroding rock that life in water and on land was made possible. And today the fertility of an area of land is still defined by the presence of mineral substances and an adequate water supply. All organic life on the blue planet – algae, meadows, forests, fish, birds, all animals and humankind – originally owes its existence to inorganic material, that is, to stones.

The volcanic rock that was left behind by the slowly cooling Earth once the liquid magma had set solid – a process that has by no means concluded yet, but can still be observed in volcanically active areas – was in its turn eroded by heat, cold, wind and water, and formed deposits and sediments, which in the course of time once again became compressed into new rock formations. The motive force for this revolutionary process was the movement of the great tectonic plates, releasing the energies that allowed mountain ranges to be created and, with the help of gravity, enormously accelerating the reshaping of the Earth's surface. These processes, taking place over almost unimaginably vast periods of time, acquire a mighty dramatic force if one thinks in terms of a greater timescale than our own. In the time-lapse the surface of the Earth becomes a skin continually in motion, shaken by tremors, eruptions and a constantly changing climate. The history of the Earth is no less exciting and fascinating than the history of mankind, peoples and nations, which draws us under its spell. And just as we try to create an ever more accurate image of the past in order to better understand the present, by means of objects and documents handed down to us, so too we can learn to understand the history of the Earth ever better with the help of the materials that have been given to us – the stones.

Aerial photographs by © Bernhard Edmaier:

Above: **KIRR**, salt grassland on the Baltic coast near MECKLENBURG-WESTERN POMERANIA, GERMANY
Centre: **ALLUVIAL LAND** in the Damara mountains, NAMIB DESERT, AFRICA
Below: **SAND DUNES** after a rain shower with sparse greenery, NAMIB DESERT, AFRICA

Above: **GRAMADULLAS**, rock labyrinth in the NAMIB DESERT, AFRICA
Centre: **SALT LAKES AND SALT DEPOSITS**, CARRIZO PLAIN, CALIFORNIA, USA
Below: **RIVERS** in the ORD-RIVER-DELTA, WESTERN AUSTRALIA

Above: **TSONDABVLEI**, lake basin between dunes, NAMIB DESERT, AFRICA
Centre: **ESTUARY AREA, DEEP CREEK**, near BROOME, WESTERN AUSTRALIA
Below: **GROSSER OSTERSEE** near PENZBERG, SOUTHERN GERMANY

Aerial photograph from 2500m | Pattern of currents on the BAHAMA-BANK near ELENTHERA, BAHAMAS (Photograph: © Bernhard Edmaier)

OPAL | COOBER PEDY, AUSTRALIA
Blue as the sea

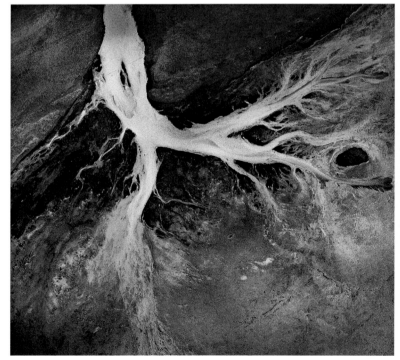

Aerial photograph of a river on the LANDEYJAR, SANDER, SOUTH ICELAND (Photograph: © Bernhard Edmaier)

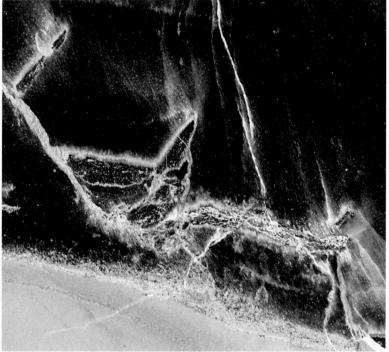

TIGER-HAWK'S EYE | SOUTH AFRICA
Rivers and deltas

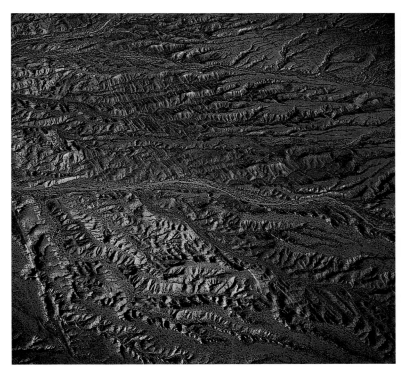

Aerial photograph of a rocky landscape to the west of
LAKE MEAD, NEVADA, USA (Photograph: © Bernhard Edmaier)

PETRIFIED WOOD (LOCUST) | OREGON, USA
This petrified wood dates back to the Miocene epoch and is 15–25 million years old.

Aerial photograph of sand islands in LAKE AMADEUS,
AUSTRALIA (Photograph: © Bernhard Edmaier)

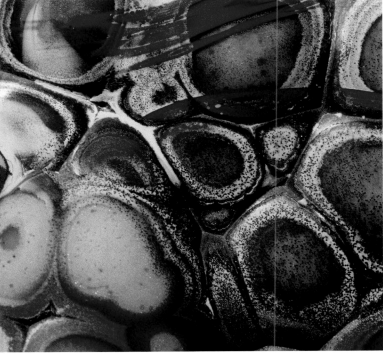

CRAZY LACE AGATE | CHIHUAHUA, MEXICO
Unusual round agglomeration and red lines, found in an agate

DRY CRACKS IN A RIVERBED | SWAKOP RIVER,
NAMIBIA, AFRICA (close-up)
(Photograph: © Bernhard Edmaier)

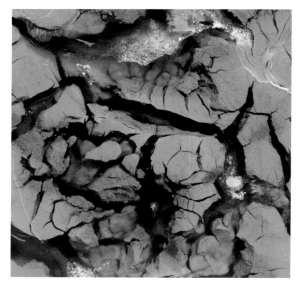

AGATE | SICILY, ITALY
What looks like a dried-up lake is actually the inside of
an agate.

THE MAGIC OF POLISHED SURFACES

For years Georg Kern has been concerned with the world of
stones, a world full of fascinating beauty, with brilliant
colours and radiant light.

Like all collectors, he was fascinated by large mineral
examples, but their size was only the beginning for him. In
such a piece, one sees the form of the crystal to the best
advantage, determined as it is by the chemical composition
of the mineral.

But the wonderful world of crystals is also found on a
much smaller scale. If we can only enlarge enough, we can
find the same wonderful crystals in the smallest parts as in
the larger pieces. Using the stereomicroscope, with the
tiniest samples one can enter into crystal caves that are not
usually accessible on a larger scale, unless one goes to the
trouble of discovering these for oneself.

Nevertheless, even with optical aids one still always
remains on the surface of minerals. One can only really
penetrate the stone by cutting it, a technique which mankind
has mastered and put to use over the centuries.

Even in the earliest days, floors and walls were covered
with cut stones: temples, palaces, museums and schools
were clad with marble to lend dignity, grandeur and
durability. But stones were also cut into round shapes
and pierced for use as chains and jewellery. In marble halls
and in the books and caskets adorned with cut stones we
see the results of these attempts to bring the inner beauty
of stones to the surface and make it visible.

It is not surprising, therefore, that it is a physician who
has achieved insight into inaccessible inner rooms, for
after all it is medicine that has succeeded in recent years,
by means of x-ray machines, computer tomographs,
magnetic resonance devices, and combinations of all these,

SOUTH AMERICAN NOCTUID MOTH | This camouflage
is strikingly similar to petrified wood.

PETRIFIED WOOD | OREGON, USA
Cypress wood from the Miocene epoch, 15–25 million
years old.

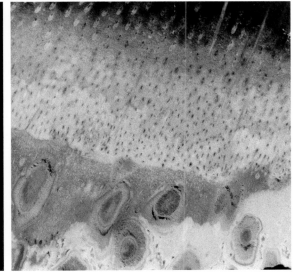

PEACOCK BUTTERFLY | The butterfly species we know
today have existed for more than 50 million years.

PETRIFIED WOOD | STINKING WATER, OREGON, USA
The structures and colours of the butterfly's wings are
rediscovered in the stone.

in achieving a three-dimensional insight into the human
body, to make it accessible for analysis and diagnosis.

MACROCOSM AND MICROCOSM

Humans, gazing at the firmament, have always been in awe of the expanse of the universe in which they have lived. And ever since human thoughts were first handed down to us, philosophers have always contemplated the idea that the very great elements in the universe corresponded to the small things on our planet – and vice versa. Astronomers and atomic scientists were quick to observe this correspondence, and they developed atomic models in which the protons and electrons move according to the harmony of the heavenly bodies. But in addition to this almost prosaic physical interpretation of the world, mystics of all ages have intuitively perceived that the world of the small is mirrored in the world of the large – and the other way around. Paracelsus, Leibnitz, and even Goethe were guided by such thoughts. Moreover, mystics have at all times been convinced that infinity, the very great, or God, finds a correspondence in the very small, for example in the human soul, which thus becomes part of a surrounding entity, a small spark of the great fire, the divine part of us. But no one was more profoundly convinced that the same principles of nature can be found throughout the universe than Goethe:

> *Wär nicht das Auge sonnenhaft,*
> *die Sonne könnt es nie erblicken;*
> *läg nicht in uns des Gottes eigne Kraft,*
> *wie könnt uns Göttliches entzücken.*

> If the eye were not like the sun,
> it could never see the sun;
> if God's own power were not within us,
> how could anything divine delight us?

The vision of primeval unity between the great surrounding entity and the individual and small is one of the most characteristic elemental experiences that has determined the thinking of humankind in intellectual history. The correspondence between, indeed even perhaps the identification of, the macrocosmic and the microcosmic gives humankind its greatness, its dignity, but also its integration into the totality of creation. The harmony of the heavenly bodies and the structure of atoms are mirrored in the congruence of eternal durability and the individual lives of humans, which becomes a symbol of the encircling whole. Ancient philosophers, neo-Platonists and contemporary thinkers have drawn vitality and a sense of the meaning of life from this parallelism, and countless works of art owe their power to this insight.

But let us return to the basis of the mineral reality of the world. An important chapter in this book is concerned with the fact that the world seen from satellites shows striking parallels with the images of cut and polished stones. In many agates, we seem to see our own planet. One glance passes over lakeland areas, deserts and dune landscapes, river estuaries, islands and fjords. This astonishing parallel is the first thing to catch the eye of the observer who examines the photographs of Georg Kern. Anyone who has ever seen satellite images in atlases or on documentaries can immediately make out the kinship of the images. The recognition effect is stunning, and fills one with a comforting sense of cosmic unity.

Since everything is subject to the laws of nature, and matter everywhere obeys the same rules of chemistry and physics, this is not inexplicable, but it does not alter the fact that it astonishes us when we are presented with images on totally different scales which are similar to the point of confusion.

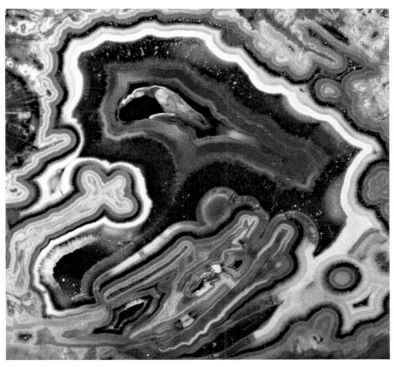

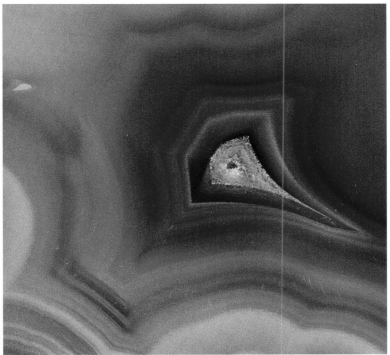

SAURIAN BONE FILLED WITH AGATE (cross-section)
RIO NEGRO, PATAGONIA, ARGENTINA (Photograph: © Robert Noll)

LAGUNA AGATE | CHIHUAHUA, MEXICO

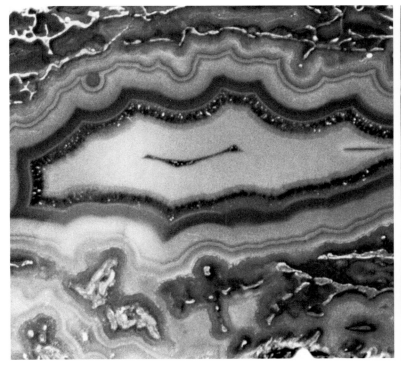

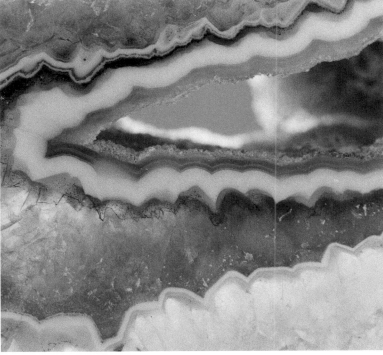

SAURIAN BONE FILLED WITH AGATE | RIO NEGRO,
PATAGONIA, ARGENTINA (Photograph: © Robert Noll)

AGATE | BRAZIL

LYONEL FEININGER | 'EICHELBORN',
oil on canvas, 1920, State Museums, Berlin,
National Gallery © VG Bild-Kunst,
Bonn 2004

The structures of mixtures, rhythmic lines and wavy surfaces always obey the same laws and the sight of them fascinates us, whether we are gazing out across the wide ocean, observing the wonderful regularity of a leaf or taking in the structure of a polished stone, as presented by Georg Kern with the lens of his camera.

IN THE PLAY OF ASSOCIATIONS AND VISIONS

These stones, cut into thin slices and polished, on the one hand reveal some of their secrets, but on the other they pose new puzzles. It was only one more short step, but an important one, to preserve these new findings in photographs. Here too it was know-how, experimentation and finally experience that were needed. The result is impressive.

The images enable a powerful insight into the innermost part of the stones, but they also surprise us with a multiplicity of forms and colours which we, freed from all questions of mineralogy, can simply come to know as an inspiring world of wonders. Our psyche reacts to the photographs like subjects of a Rorschach ink-blot test. It begins to make wild associations, ideas crowd in from all areas of life, comparisons with living nature emerge, or one believes one sees faces, figures, animals in the cut stone.

One can however simply just look at the photographs, try to approach them in a less intellectual or emotional manner, and let the effect of their beauty work upon one in a meditative state. The photographs in the end are not so far away from works of art. Admittedly the images are not created, but only found in the stone. But one must have had the eye to see and the confidence to choose the right cut. From the world buried in the depths of the Earth, images of enigmatic beauty are brought into the light of day. Hardly less than the stones themselves, their models, these images reproduce with astonishing accuracy the interaction between striking, reflected light and translucent light. Most

VERDE D'ARNO | FLORENCE, ITALY
What looks like abstract art is actually a section from a
limestone slab.

GEORGIA O'KEEFFE | 'DARK IRIS II',
oil on canvas, 1926, © VG Bild-Kunst, Bonn 2004

minerals after all are neither entirely transparent nor totally opaque. On the contrary, with almost all these images a third dimension is created by a certain degree of transparency. It is as though one could look through the surface right into the stone. This is particularly the case with the agates, quartz stones which are usually partly translucent.

This effect is even more striking in the opals and the opalescent minerals. No one can escape their charm. The water enclosed in the crystalline lattice of quartz reflects direct sunlight and allows a spectrum of colours to light up, as do raindrops with a rainbow. But in the crystal lattice the colours are even more diffused, more radiant and more enigmatic. According to legend, a treasure is buried where the rainbow touches the Earth, and the closer one approaches the spot, the farther away the rainbow recedes. A symbol of the unattainability of absolute happiness, and also for the fact that beauty cannot be captured, but only admired from a respectful distance. Goethe once mocked the attempt to identify the charm of a poem by means of interpretation. It was, he argued logically, as though one were to dismantle with a chisel the famous salt-cellar of Benvenuto Cellini (which had just been lost in Vienna) with the aim of discovering the secret of its beauty.

Dr Andreas Honegger

AGATE | NESSELHOF, THURINGIA, GERMANY
Shell-shaped lines in an agate

SHIMMERING BEAUTY

SHIMMERING BEAUTY

1 | **OPAL** | COOBER PEDY, AUSTRALIA

Ink-blue shades in a glassy material. It is thanks to the nature of the stone that the individual zones of the photograph appear in varied sharpness. Varied densities permit views of varied depth. In deeper regions, the opaque structure clouds the view to the eye.

A good example of how difficult or even impossible it is to explain the beauty of these stones in rational terms is offered by the images of opals found in this book. Certainly, we discover their beauty because they have been cut, but we cannot venture behind the polished surface, only allow our eyes to stray dreamily through this magical forest of colours and forms.

THE BLUE OF THE SEA AND TROPICAL BUTTERFLIES

Like the view from a high cliff of the most varied tones of blue in a tropical ocean, or the most beautiful parts of the Côte d'Azur, so is the sight of blue opals. Dark azure merges into powerful turquoise (see previous pages). Waves and rocks seem to play with each other in the blazing midday sunlight (1, 2). The various shades shine like shimmering silk, or some other exquisite fabric. But isn't there a glint of white ice as well (4)? This blue is not the blue of the warm Mediterranean or of a Caribbean beach. It is a cold, fixed glitter, the reflected light of the water molecules held captive as if frozen deep in the crystal lattice of the quartz. A landscape full of shimmering secrets, fractures and abysses.

Another time it is the dazzling wings of a tropical butterfly (3) that this stone could well put in the shade. Like the glistening blue on the wings of a Brazilian butterfly, the opal glows in its matrix.

2 | **OPAL** | COOBER PEDY, AUSTRALIA
Filled with light, as on southern shores

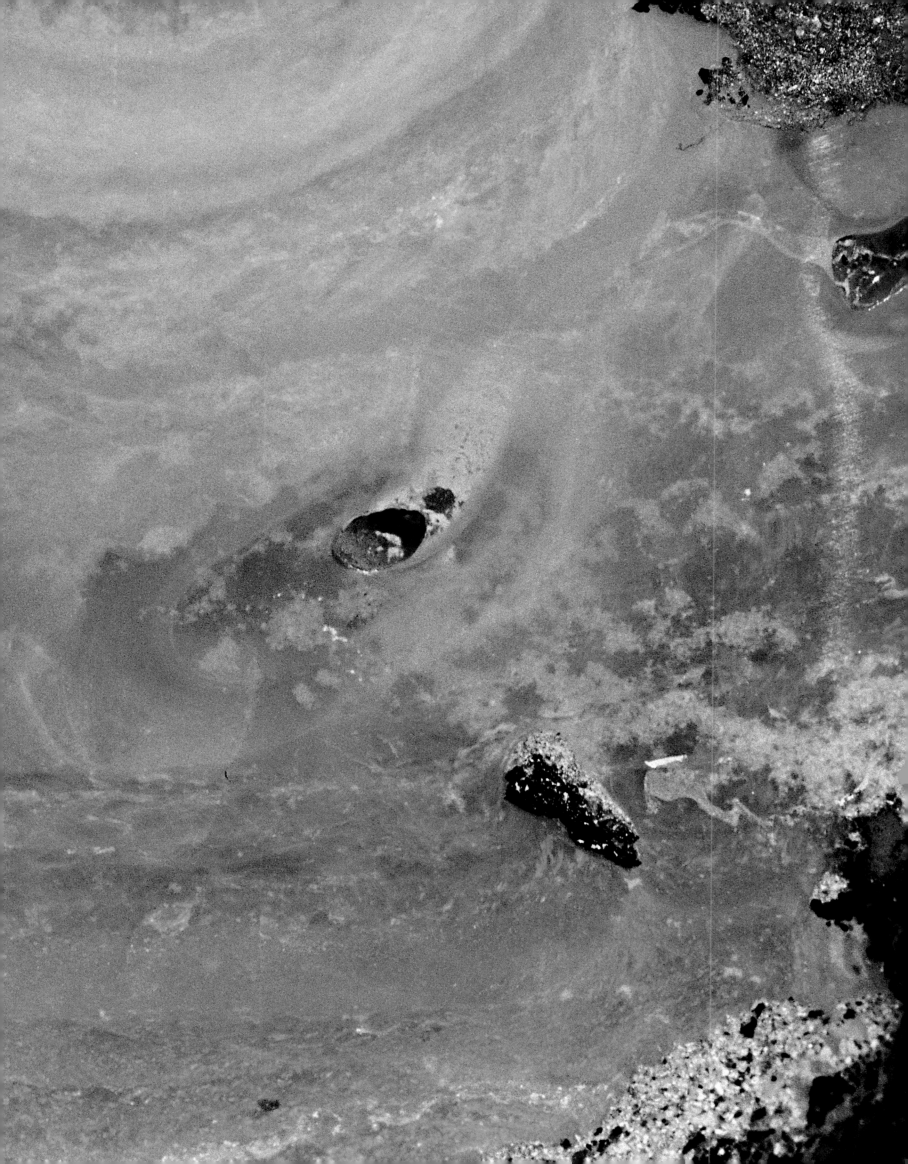

3 | **OPAL** | COOBER PEDY, AUSTRALIA
The vein of opal in the matrix forms an interesting H-shaped figure, reminiscent of tropical butterflies.

4 | **OPAL** | COOBER PEDY, AUSTRALIA
A simply beautiful but cool landscape that invites one to dream. The opal, shimmering in blue-green, and slight splinters of quartz, appearing almost white, are part of this landscape.

FIBROUS ...

From the mother-of-pearl sheen of opals, it is not far to the fibrous play of light of the Tiger's Eye (5, 6). The image holds fast the golden radiance against a dark background, and with these crocidolite fibres we notice, for almost the only time, a shortcoming in the photograph compared to the original – the shifting effect is lost. Normally, by slightly moving the object, the area of the Tiger's Eye with the golden reflection can be set in motion, as with shot silk, or, indeed, the eye of a beast of prey. The comparison with textiles is unavoidable – and not by chance, for here too there are fibres that form the structure and break up and reflect the light. Like immensely precious brocade, embroidered with old, oxidized silver thread, are the Tiger Irons from Australia (7, 8): costly shawls that, with their flaming red, could belong to a Spanish dancer; or are these the streams of glowing magma that flow idly down to the valley in narrow meanders between solidified lava?

6 | **TIGER'S EYE** | SOUTH AFRICA
The black interrupted line that runs like an inscription through this Tiger's Eye lends a special tension to the stone.

5 | **TIGER'S EYE** | SOUTH AFRICA
The fibres in the Tiger's Eye, running parallel, allow the shiny areas, lighting up with gold, to move to and fro when the stone is moved. The dark fracture area where the fibres are broken up conveys the effect of a cut in a textile fabric.

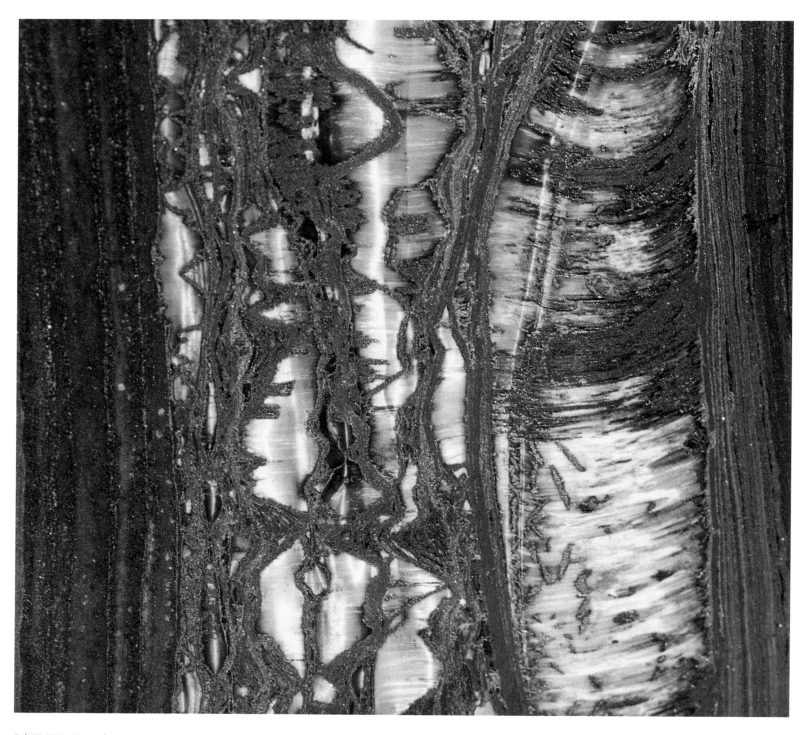

7 | **TIGER IRON** | AUSTRALIA
In the Tiger Iron, dark silver and red supplement the golden
tones – like gold brocade detailing geological eras.

8 | **TIGER IRON** | AUSTRALIA
The soft folds of this Tiger Iron remind one of
costly materials.

... AND FURRY

The fibres of the Tiger's Eye and Hawk's Eye, shimmering in warm gold, remind us on the one hand of the needles of rutile caged in their cold prison of crystal glass (9), and on the other of the fibrous structure of the petrified wood, an inorganic parody of a formerly organic material, which calls for comparison with birds' feathers or fur (10–13). The stone simulates a cuddly warmth and pleasant softness, which lies inaccessibly beneath the polished coldness of the surface. Here too, as the pictures show, the comparison with the structure of butterflies' wings is obvious. But the regular arrangement of the fibres (10) may also remind us of a marsh overgrown with reeds or grass, or of the wintry aspect of a garden laid out in a modern style.

Certainly it is not by accident that these petrified, formerly organic, materials remind us above all of vegetable matter, of plants, but also of animals. Again and again, we allow ourselves to be carried away thinking of new associations of the image, but in that way, describing and circumscribing, we come back to the sensations that were seized upon at the first glance. A comparatively disagreeable association with large hairy spiders is aroused by the pietersite from Namibia (14, 15), even if its play of forms and colours has a highly exciting effect. It could also be a less intimidating insect, the delicate scales of the structure of a moth, or even a summer bird. On the other hand, the petrified wood from Washington and Oregon, many millions of years old (16, 17), has the structure of a wildcat's hide, which one would like to stroke, if it were not for the danger ...

9 | **NEEDLES OF RUTILE IN QUARTZ** | VAL AUL, GRISONS, SWITZERLAND
The delicate needles of rutile in this rock crystal from the Swiss Alps look like frozen blades of grass in a block of ice.

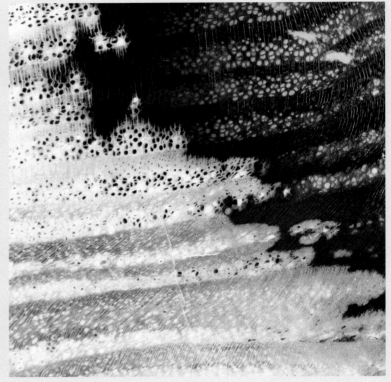

10 | **PETRIFIED CYPRESS WOOD** | OREGON, USA
The fine, fibrous structure in a piece of petrified sequoia wood
looks like rows of grass or reeds moved by the wind.

11 | **PETRIFIED LOCUST WOOD** | OREGON, USA
The form and colours of this petrified wood are reminiscent
of birds' feathers.

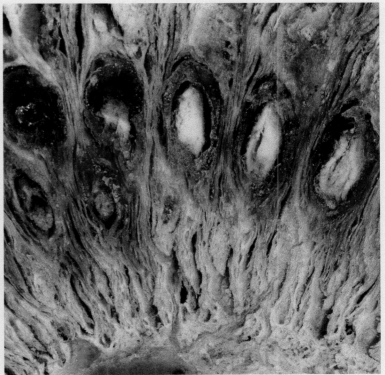

12 | **PETRIFIED WOOD** | OREGON, USA
This petrified wood from the Miocene period is about 15–25
million years old. The structure of the wood has been
preserved, but the organic substance has been entirely
replaced by quartz.

13 | **PETRIFIED WOOD** | PATAGONIA, ARGENTINA
Araucaria mirabilis from the Jura period is 100–140 million
years old. One could easily believe it to be the feathered
garment of a bird.

14 | **PIETERSITE** | OUTJO, NAMIBIA, AFRICA
This pietersite, a Ruin Hawk's Eye, is characterized by
enigmatic forms and colours.

15 | **PIETERSITE** | OUTJO, NAMIBIA, AFRICA

The history of the origin of this stone is complex. As with the
Tiger's Eye, this is a pseudomorphosis of crocidolite, a variety of
riebeckite. This means that the original material is replaced by
quartz, but retains its original form and structure. Thus the
Hawk's Eye is created, from whose debris a new stone is formed
from quartz: pietersite.

16 | **PETRIFIED WOOD** | WASHINGTON, USA
This petrified wood, 15–25 million years old, still has its
annual rings; but in addition to these, other substances have
been deposited, giving the stone its appearance of tension.

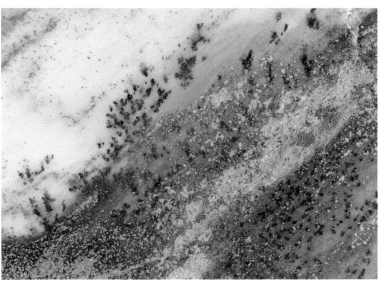

17 | **PETRIFIED WOOD** | OREGON, USA
The palette of colours ranges from white through yellow and
orange to black.

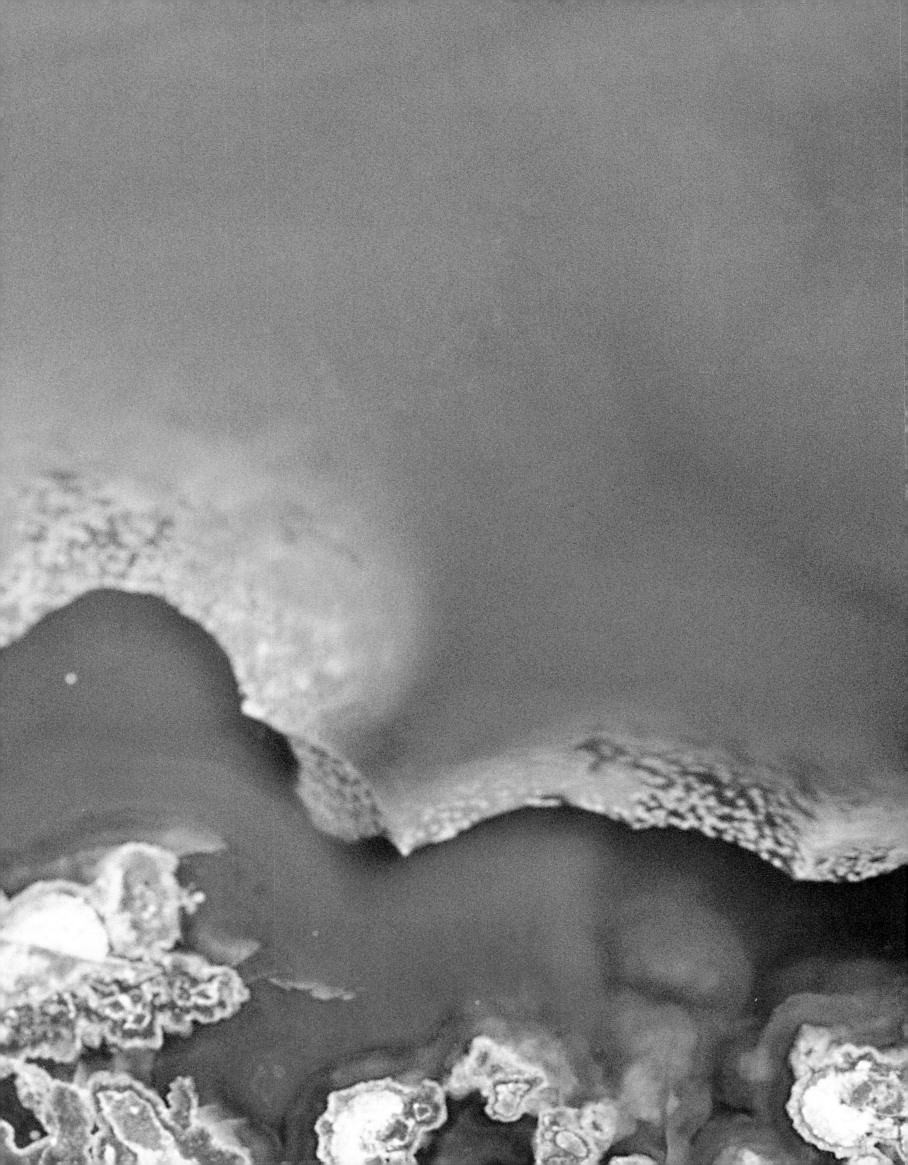

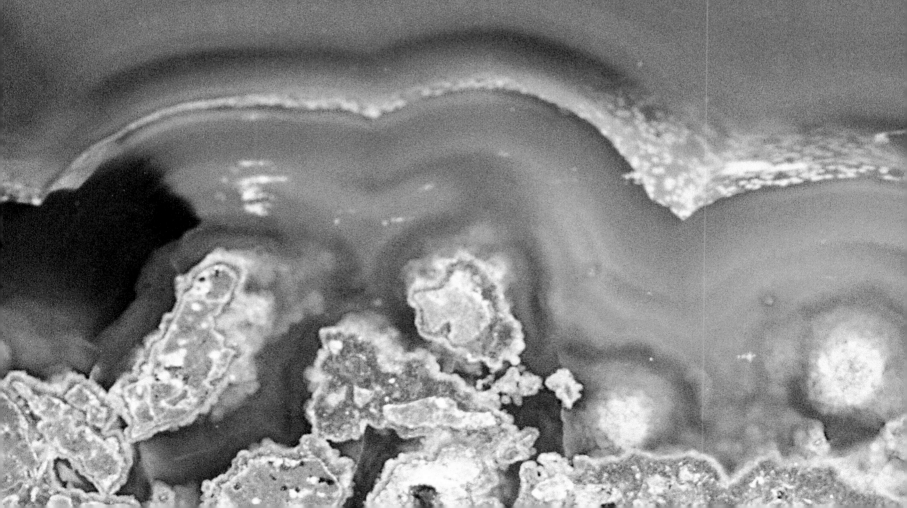

AGATES AND THEIR PLAY OF WAVES

AGATES AND THEIR PLAY OF WAVES

It is not by chance that agates are so well represented in this book, for their play of forms and colours is enchanting. Their charm lies in the contrast of gentle, soft gradations of colour and knife-sharp lines of separation, running in more or less parallel curves and waves. These band structures naturally remind us of the annual rings in the wood of felled trees, and presumably they came into being in a similar way. Depending on the quantity and quality of the material, the fine, amorphous growth of crystals progressed at a faster or slower rate, and the material was coloured more or less strongly by metal oxides. Each agate has a charm of its own, but the presence of so many in this book allows one to recognize very quickly the conformity that they all manifest.

CASHMERE PATTERNS AND AARON'S RODS

The spherical, tear-shaped growth – together with its shades of red and orange – often evokes the ornamental forms of elegant jacquard fabrics interwoven with gold, or Indian Kashmiri patterns (1–3). Kashmiri woven fabrics reached Europe at the end of the 18th century and under Napoleon's Empire they became the last word in fashion in high society. Soon cashmere shawls of the highest quality were being made in French factories. But the shawls achieved their wide popularity through their industrial production in Scotland, where the fabrics were both woven and printed. Edinburgh was the first centre of production, followed by Paisley, which gave its name to the pattern. Cashmere shawls were also made in Norwich, and later in America.

Just as the tear-shaped pattern of the cashmere shawl often has an empty centre, so the rounded forms of the agate surround pointed, almost geometric forms in their inner depth. To an extent these fill the gaps between the dominant forms, but for that very reason they draw the gaze towards themselves, a crowning centre of tension. Finely dotted red lines strengthen the textile effect, but also remind one of glue paintings produced by a comb on paper (4–8).

The innermost core of the agate is framed like a precious stone, often in almost square or rhombic frames (5). When the material for the formation of crystals was almost exhausted, a few last delicate crystals could still be formed in the innermost depth of an agate around an opening, for example as in the beautiful red-rimmed agate from Brazil.

The dramatic interplay of circular forms with acute-angled, often almost straight geometric lines opens a wide field to our imagination: is this (6) a bird standing here, frozen in stone for years? The play of agate waves in white, red and brown often has an almost musical rhythm (7, 8). Can we see syncopations here, images of sound, waves that concentrated on a precise oscillation only to peter out again into diffuseness?

Each stone seems to be signed with the characteristic style of an artist or calligrapher. Here a part of the geological history of our planet has been 'written' in a handwriting not accessible to our intellect.

1 | **AGATE** | RIO GRANDE DO SUL, BRAZIL
The powerful red and the light, crusty 'golden' parts of the stone are reminiscent of luxurious textiles.

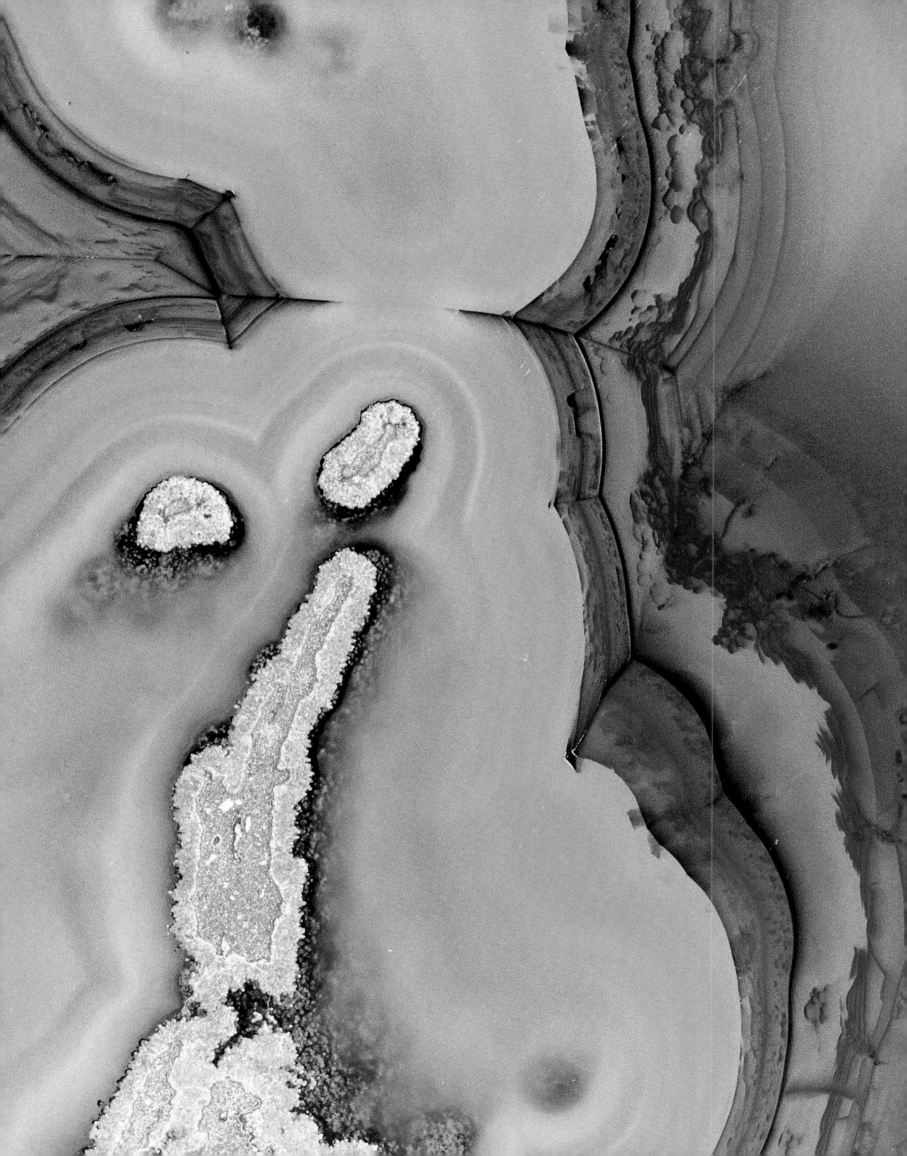

2 | **AGATE** | DRYHEAD, MONTANA, USA
The regularly distributed coloured dots enhance even
further the impression of a textile, while the alternation of
rounded and pointed forms and black surfaces enclosed in
red is also found in the cashmere fabrics that were the
height of fashion in the 19th century.

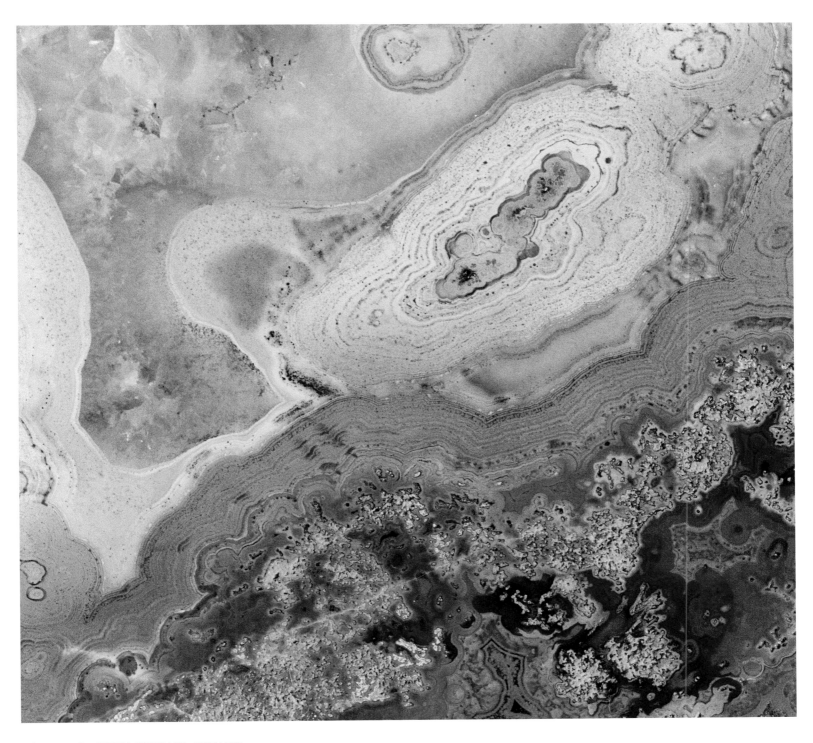

3 | **AGATE** | FREISEN, SAARLAND, GERMANY
Harmonious interplay of colours

Following pages:
4 | **CONDOR AGATE** | SAN RAFAEL, PATAGONIA, ARGENTINA
Rounded forms, parallel lines, alternating light and dark areas –
everything that goes to make a typical agate.

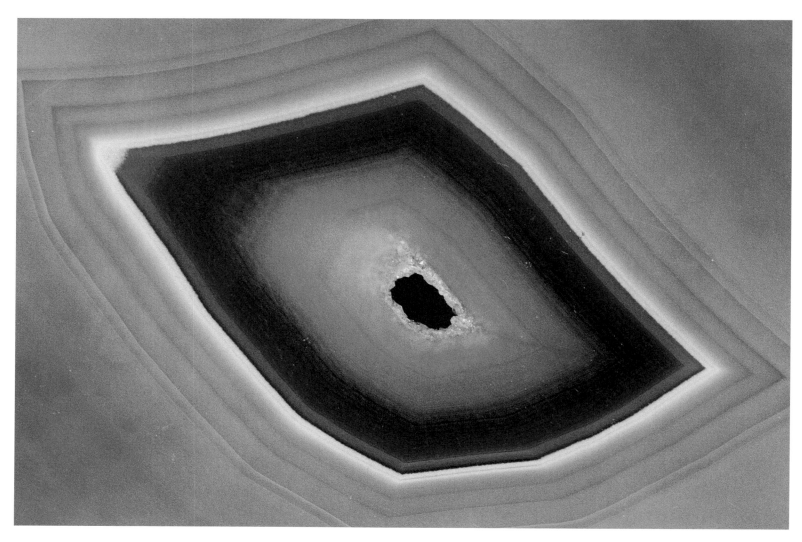

5 | **AGATE** | BRAZIL
Rhombus-shaped 'heart' of an agate in an up-light. In its
innermost depths some little rock crystals can be recognized,
which were able to form in the remaining cavity.

6 | **LAGUNA AGATE** | CHIHUAHUA, MEXICO
What looks like the body of a bird is also an area with recognizable
quartz crystals. These have finally closed up a last opening within
the agate geode.

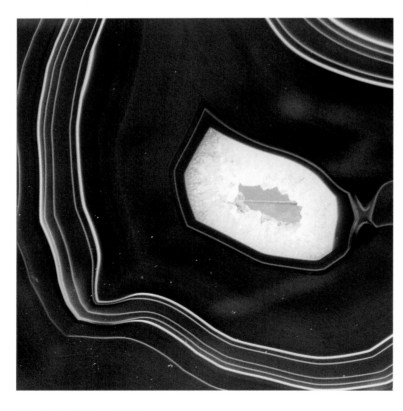

7 | SARDONYX | BRAZIL
Light-coloured lines in the dark material frame a small open window with visible crystal formation.

8 | SARDONYX | BRAZIL
Calligraphy of bright lines

JEWEL IN THE INNER CENTRE

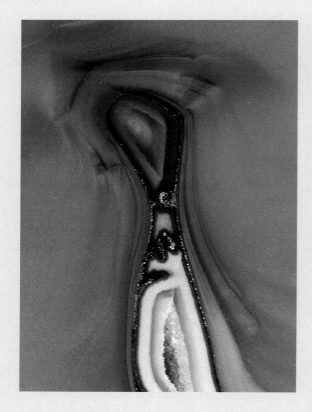

Again and again, these waves capture the eye and lead it towards the centre, towards this mystical place in the middle of the agate's structure, that obsessively draws our attention to itself like an eye, an abyss or a precious piece of jewellery (9).

The delicate parts, crystallized on a larger scale, in this innermost abyss of the agate (11–14) are like the lip of an oyster's shell, whose tender flesh has fused with the rough, crusty mineral material of the shell, or the pale yellowish flesh of the mussel in its oval black covering. These shells may not be full of pearls, but they are full of the sheen of jewels: crystal caverns set with gold chains, precious stones blazing with light, or pearls found in the soft, glowing red setting of the curving lines of the agate (15, 16). Here a jeweller has set his finest diamonds and prettiest pendants (17, 18) in gold.

9 | **AGATE** | BRAZIL
The innermost opening of the agate is seen here as though it were a small piece of jewellery set in gold.

10 | **AGATE** | QUEENSLAND, AUSTRALIA
The central point of the agate is displayed here to catch the eye, to great dramatic effect.

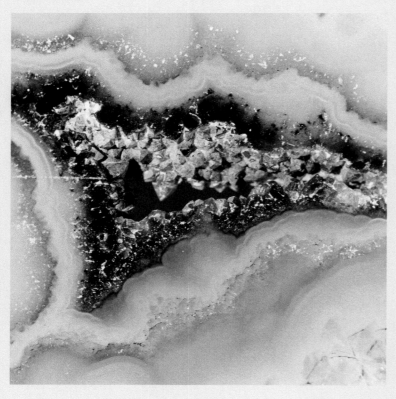

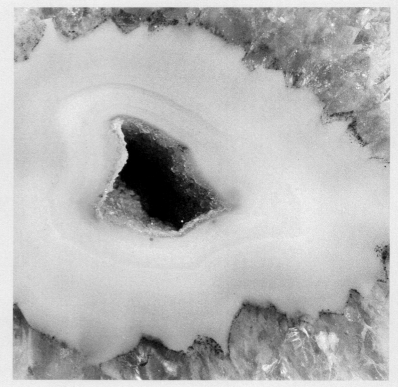

11 | **AGATE** | RIO GRANDE DO SUL, BRAZIL
Here, several rows of rock crystals enclose the last dark
opening of the agate geode.

12 | **AGATE** | BRAZIL
After large quartz crystals had formed, this agate continued
to form with microcrystalline material. At first small crystals
were formed, then a small hollow space remained.

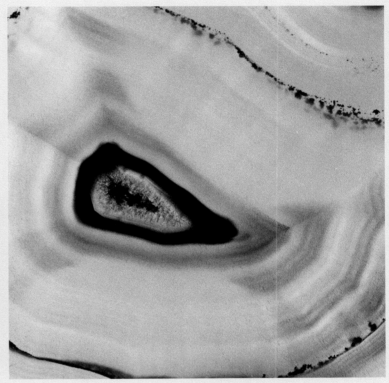

13 | **AGATE** | CHIHUAHUA, MEXICO
Shell-shaped formation: crusty forms on the outside, then various light-coloured edges that enclose the centre (not visible in the image).

14 | **AGATE** | RIO GRANDE DO SUL, BRAZIL
The graduated colours of this agate remind one of a shell or an oyster. Can you see its little pearl?

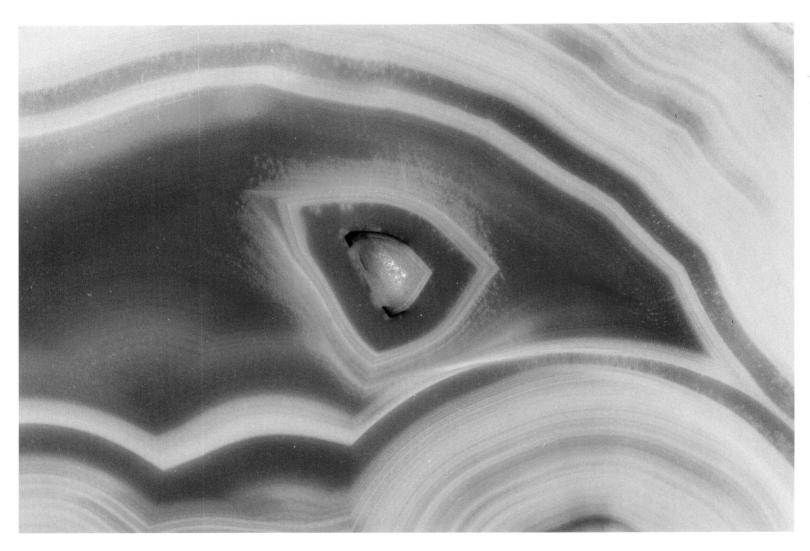

15 | **AGATE** | BRAZIL
This shining red frame also seems to enclose a pearl.

16 | **CONDOR AGATE** | SAN RAFAEL, PATAGONIA, ARGENTINA
One smaller opening in the centre of the image has closed up, while a larger one (at the upper edge of the image), formed from light-coloured crystals, has remained open.

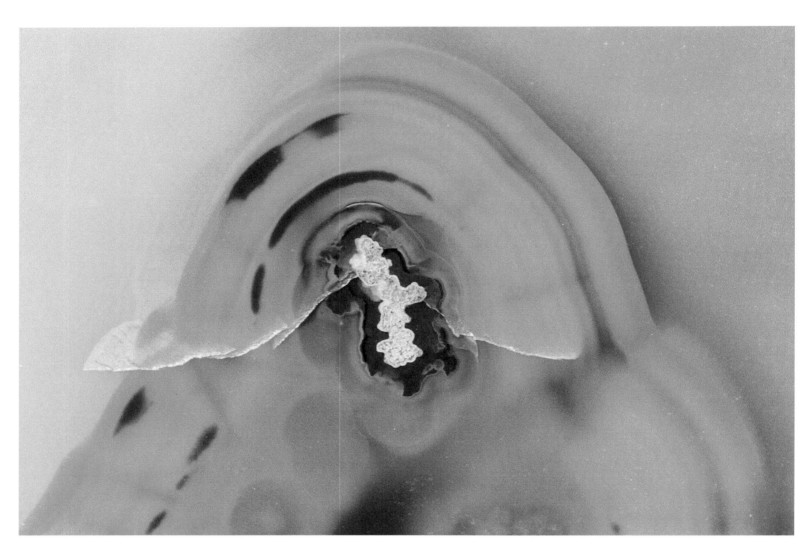

17 | **AGATE** | BRAZIL
The quartz crystals closing the centre of the agate look like a
row of small diamonds in a modern piece of jewellery.

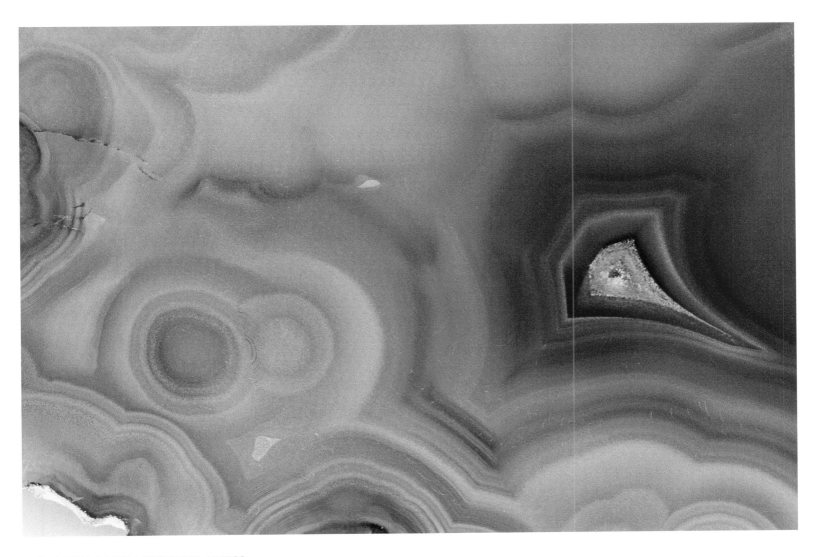

18 | **LAGUNA AGATE** | CHIHUAHUA, MEXICO
Here, to the right in the picture, a pendant seems to lie in a
jeweller's velvet-lined case.

THE SPATHE OF THE CALLA

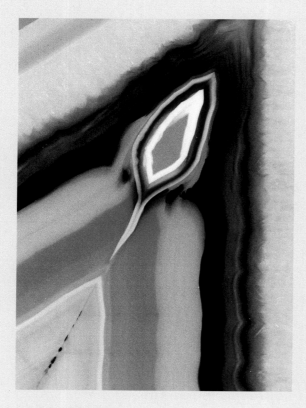

19 | AGATE | BRAZIL
The centre of this agate reminds one of an arrowhead
piercing through the stone. Cutting through the stone has
resulted in a diagonally running axis of symmetry.

No exaggerated erotic imagination is needed in order to see in
these images at least as much sexual symbolism as in the flower
paintings of a Georgia O'Keeffe. These agates are among the
most fascinating in this collection. In some (19) the image reveals
a soft axis of symmetry, with an almost biological harmony. We
may see in it arrowheads, spermatozoa, or if you prefer vegetable
comparisons, like the fruits of long-stemmed capers – but these
too often conceal a secret glittering with promise. Some seem to
lead deep into the abyss of the plant (20). It is as if we are looking
at a cross-section of a flower, with stamens and a widely
spreading pistil, which carries the suggestion of the glowing red
fruit that will develop. These flower calyces (21, 22) are attractive,
flowing plantlike on their white background. Others, in shades of
blue and yellow (23–25), form the spathe, the petals of an Aaron's
rod, some (26) seem to show not only the outer spathe of the
Aaron's rod, but also the central spadix. One agate (24) seems to
consist of a filled oyster-shaped flower. Others again are striking
for their delicate pastel shades and their correspondingly
delicate transitions. How many shades of blue, pink, beige and
olive are to be found here?

**20 | CONDOR AGATE | SAN RAFAEL, PATAGONIA,
ARGENTINA**
This cut through a diagonal axis of symmetry is like a cross-
section through a flower. The eye is directed to the bright,
glowing red centre.

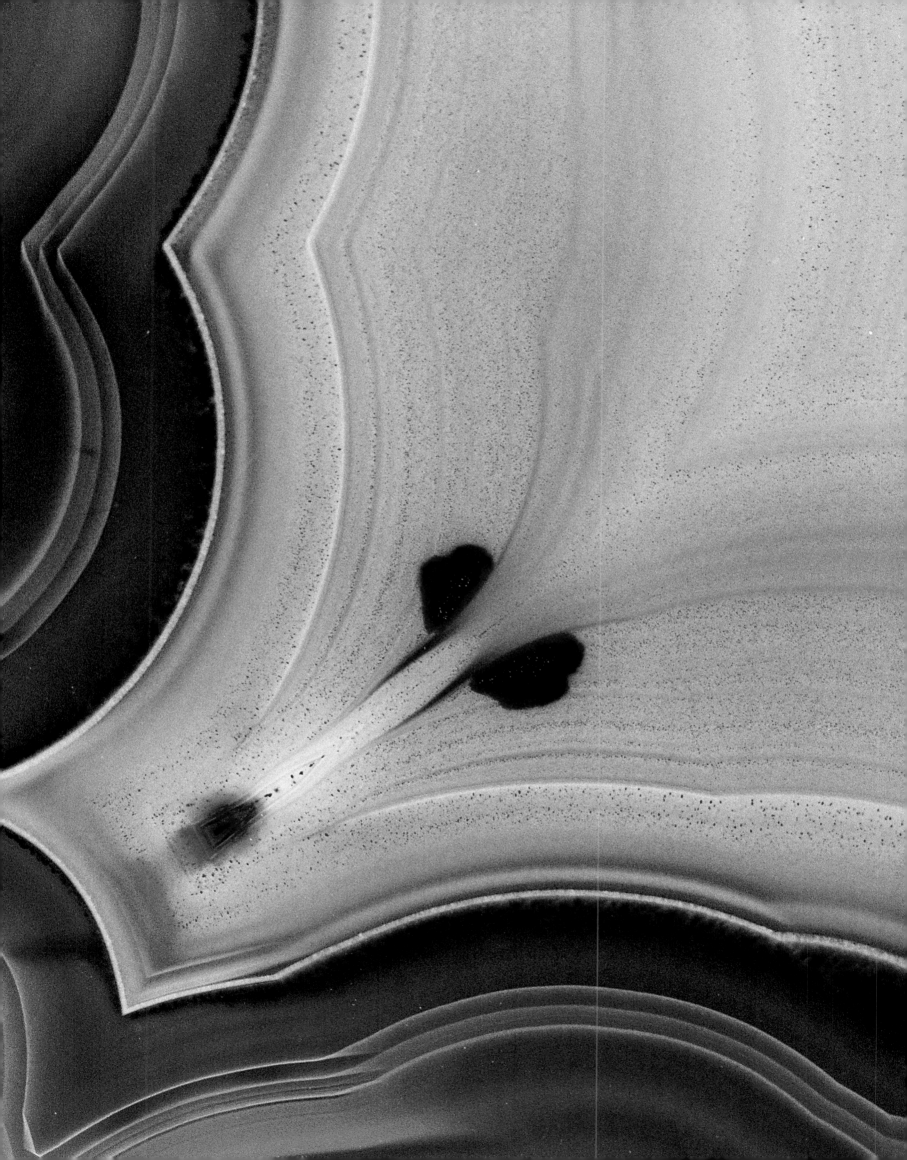

21 | **CONDOR AGATE** | SAN RAFAEL, PATAGONIA, ARGENTINA
Here too the diagonal axis of symmetry is recognizable, starting
from a light-coloured centre set in red.

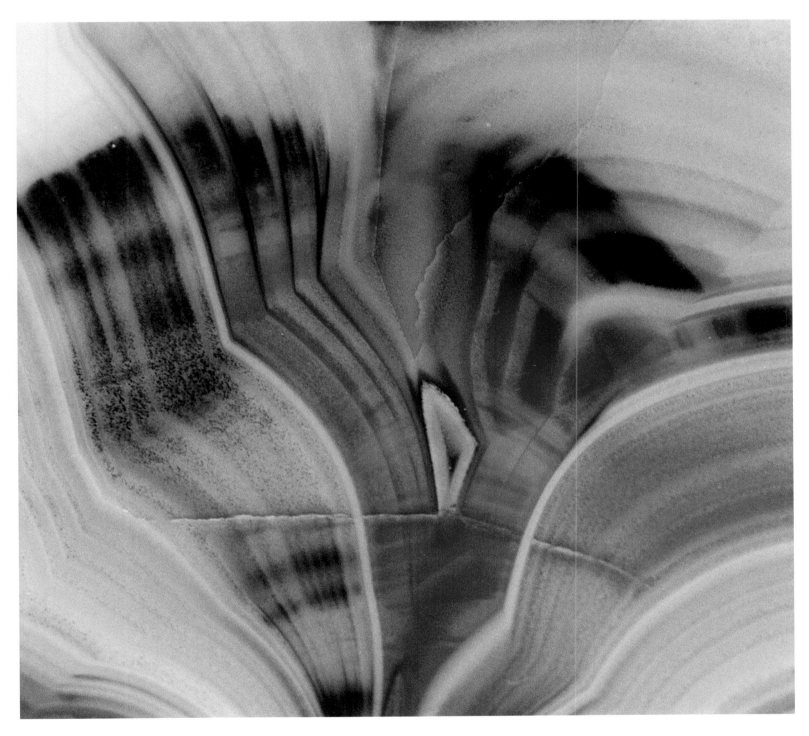

22 | **COYAMITO AGATE** | MEXICO

In this agate, movement dominates over the clear forms.
Though the course of the colours – similar to birds' feathers
– flows over the whole area of the stone, the axis and centre
are still clearly visible.

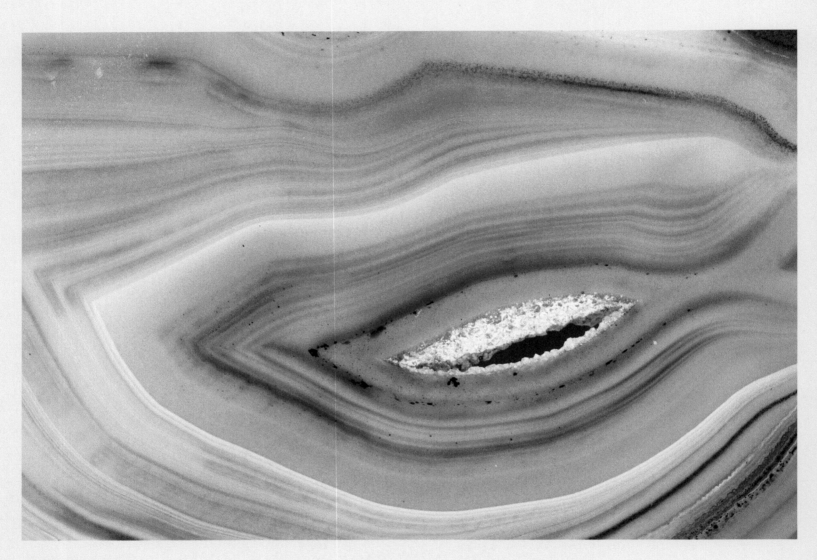

23 | AGATE | BRAZIL
Here the centre and the course of the line of symmetry are curved, forming the shape of a leaf. The charm of this image is made up of the contrast between the shining crystalline centre and its setting, as well as the delicate gradation of the shades of green.

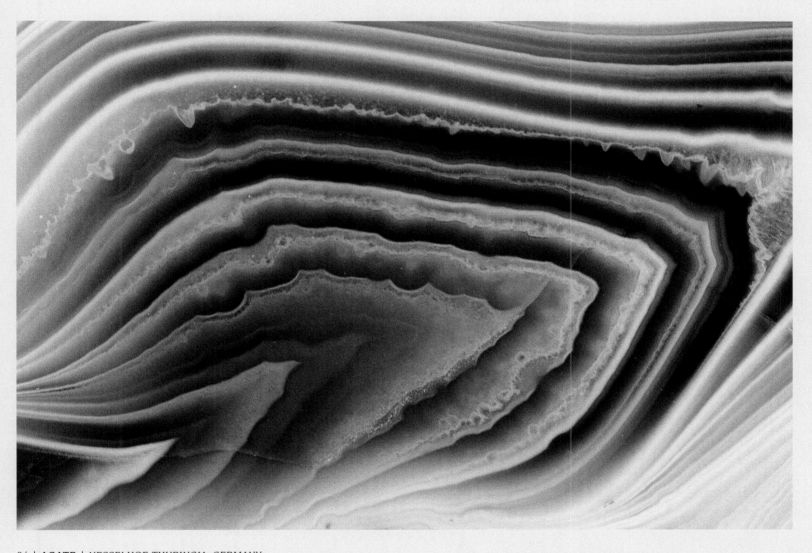

24 | **AGATE** | NESSELHOF, THURINGIA, GERMANY
Shell or leaves? The elegant curve and the shading, which
gives a sense of depth, make this stone look like something
of vegetable origin.

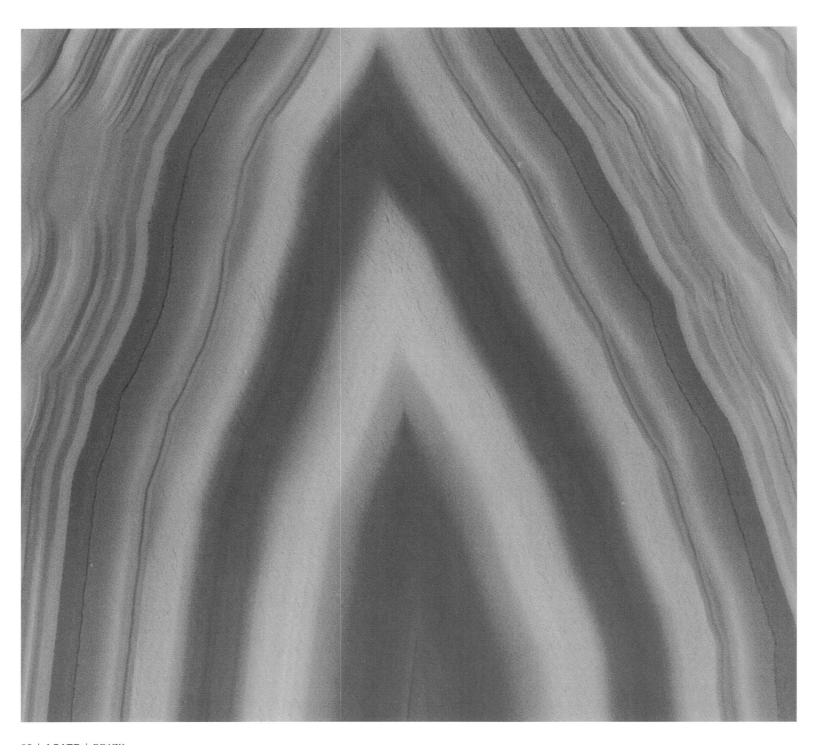

25 | **AGATE** | BRAZIL
The leaf-shaped forms are also to be found in shades of red,
thanks to the appropriate cutting of the stone.

26 | **AGATE** | BRAZIL

These leaf-shaped agates remind us of the spathe of the Aaron's rod. Here we even find the spadix that surrounds the petals. The alternation of macro- and microcrystalline material is of interest from a mineralogical point of view.

ORGANIC LIFE IN THE DEAD STONE

ORGANIC LIFE IN THE DEAD STONE

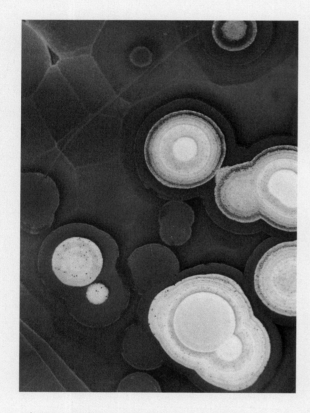

1 | **CRAZY LACE AGATE** | CHIHUAHUA, MEXICO
Merging or dividing cells under the microscope?

We often encounter images that seem to show vegetative, organic matter whose stage of development is still well below those of plants and animals: cells that merge or are at the point of dividing, for example with the Crazy Lace and Laguna Agates from Mexico (1–3). Presumably sintering has formed around various cores, which have then joined together, so that an image is created of merging or dividing cells. But these agates are also interesting because of the sculptural effect that we notice in them, like an aerial view of walled settlements that have grown together with time. And it is not in vain that the Crazy Lace Agates owe their name to slightly offbeat textile lace.

2 | **CRAZY LACE AGATE** | CHIHUAHUA, MEXICO
Enclosure or differentiation of parts; superior or inferior areas of a circle. But there always seems to be a principle of order at work.

Following pages:
3 | **CRAZY LACE AGATE** | CHIHUAHUA, MEXICO
These agates take their name from old lace covers, embroideries or bobbin-lace, which are so complicated that it takes a long time to recognize the system on which they are based.

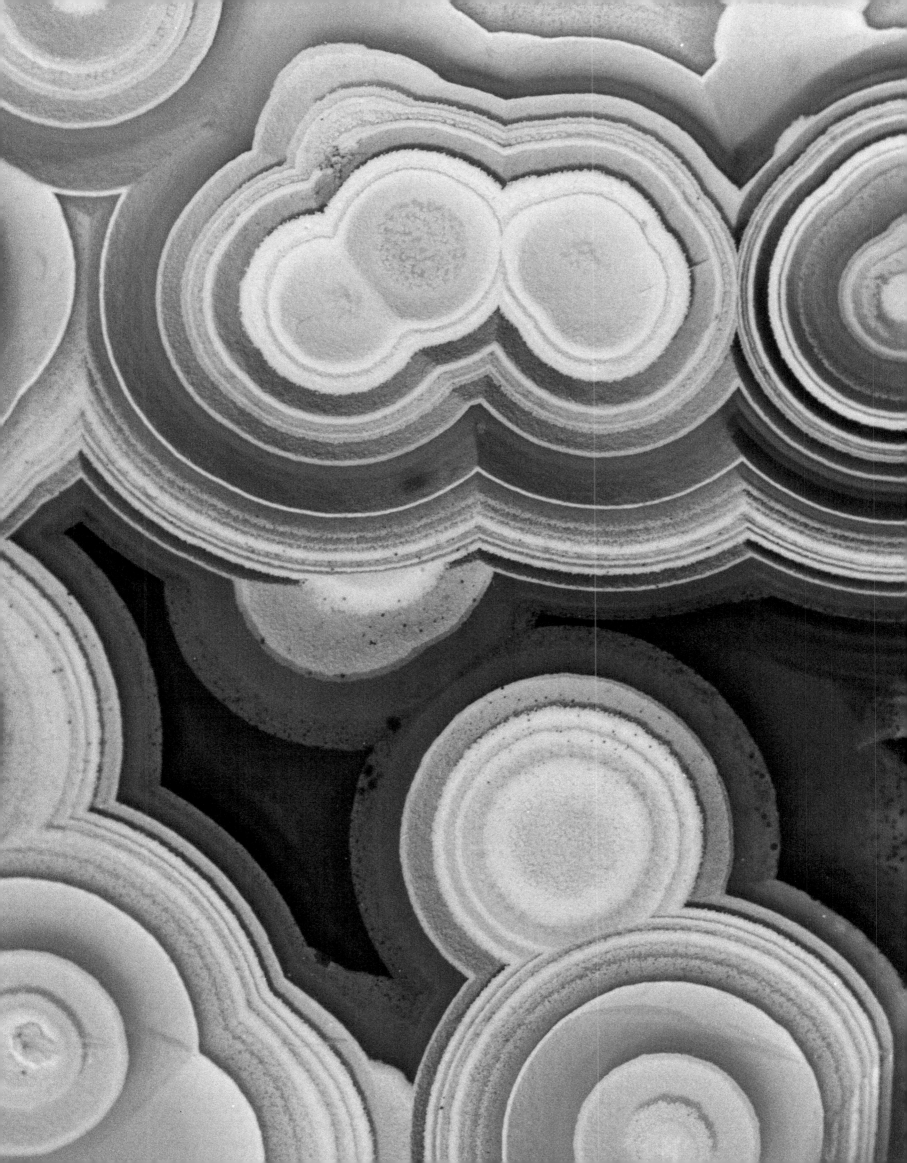

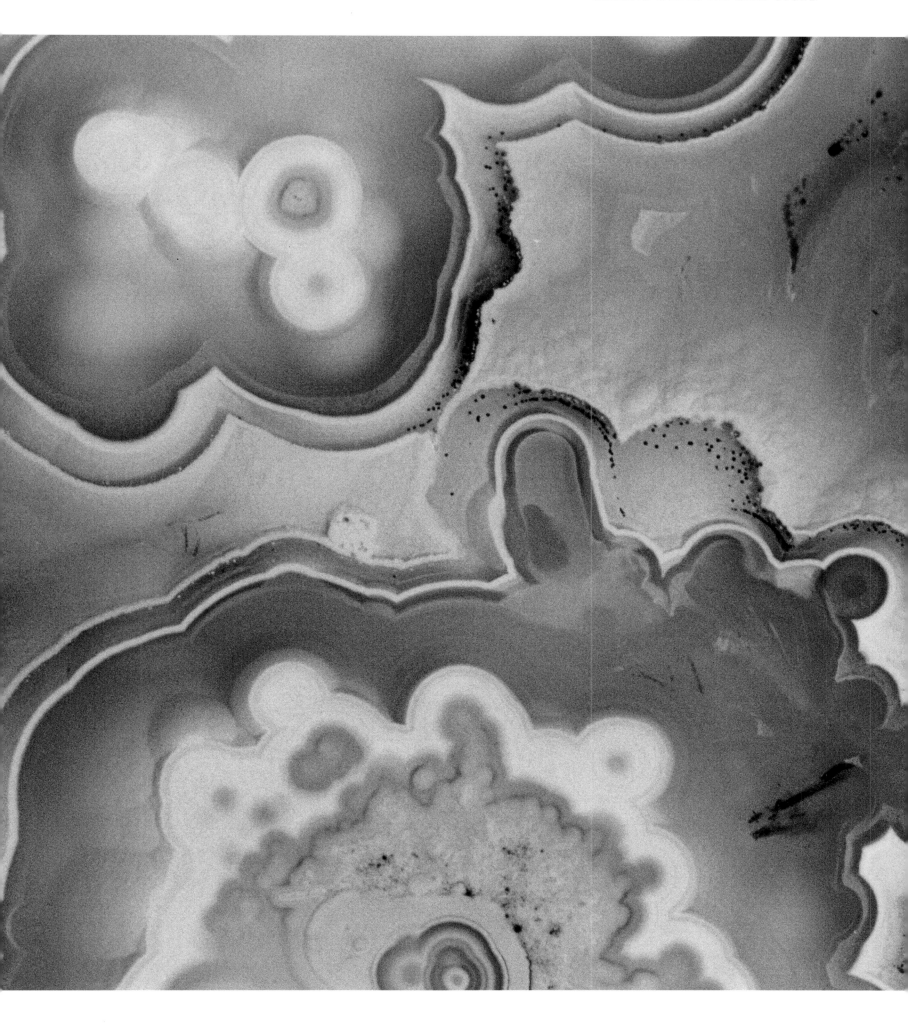

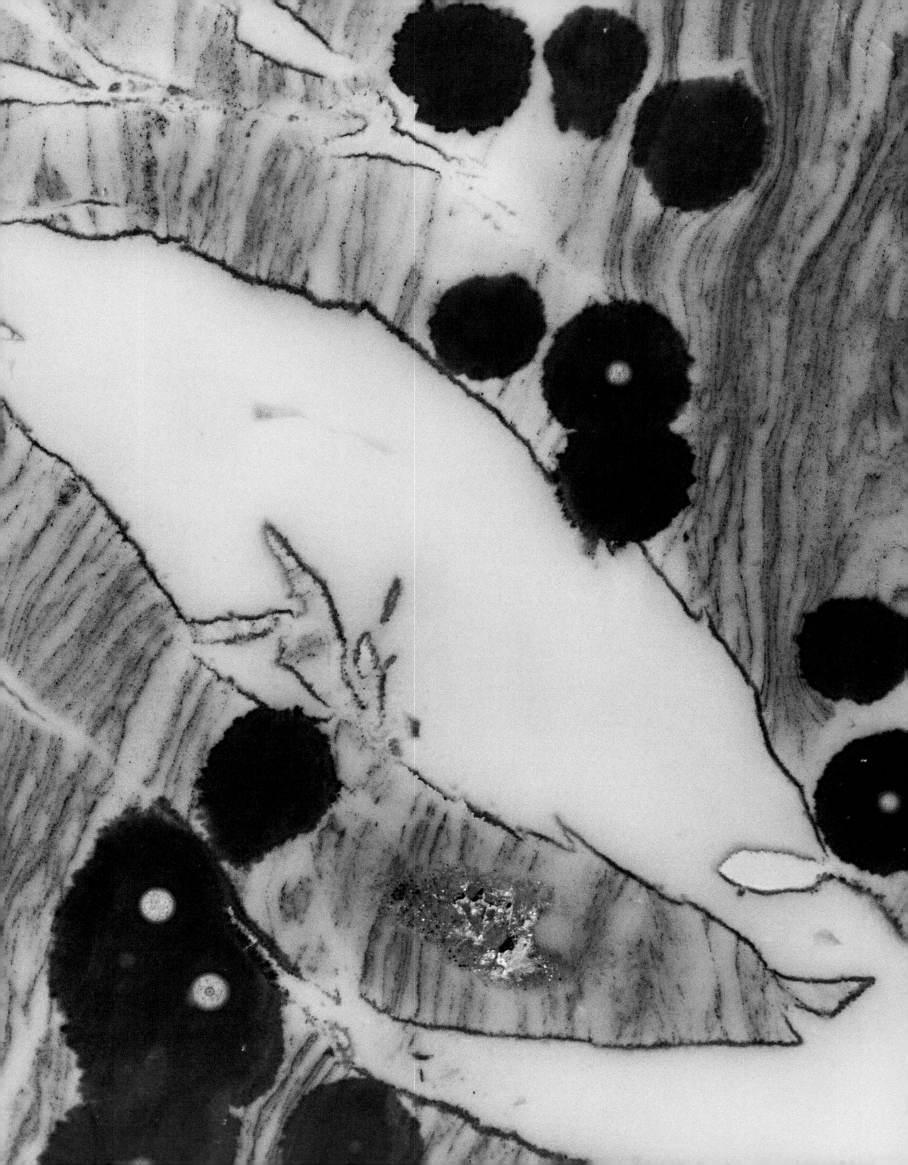

UNICELLULAR ORGANISMS AND BACTERIA

A series of mineralogically quite diverse stones evokes the association of unicellular organisms or dangerous bacteria (4–7), which seem to multiply and grow at an alarming rate. The fibrous structures of the fine crystals also remind one of the mycelial growth of fungi or bacteria on a fluid culture medium, which spread out in the form of rays.

In various colours and forms we seem to be attempting to record the number of germs in the bacterial culture. Light-coloured cores in black discs contrast with the fine lines of the stone lying between them. Shining red rounded formations are surrounded by soft covers, and they merge together as soon as the surface tension is broken, or one by one break free from the mucous membrane that forms them. Isolation and union create the tension that dominates these images. The plankton (8), water-fleas and miniature crustaceans in a pond seem to have been fixed on the slide of a microscope.

In other images (9, 10) ovoid organs with blood vessels are growing, whether to develop into amphibians, other living creatures, or even evil monsters. The expressionless eyes of a demon or an alien (11, 12) are suddenly turned upon the observer. Sombre atmospheres (13) with ghostly visages confront us, menacing protuberances in dark shades, in whose innermost hollows a maggot-like being appears to be growing (14). Or is this the decisive encounter between a well-organized, rounded, concentric dark area with a rather amorphous, dissipated, brightly shining system. Is it the struggle between two principles, 'good' versus 'evil'?

Images are there to excite our imagination, they call for interpretation – and there is no reason not to take part in this exciting game.

Observers will each have their own ideas, which are to a certain extent influenced by the image, but also largely by their own world of dreams and ideas, and by the backgrounds of their own lives.

The Bruneau Jasper from Idaho, USA, with its phallic, fungal shape (15) and fleshy, piled-up curves (16) could easily have been taken from an anatomical book or a catalogue of contemporary sculpture. Petrified wood from the Eocene era (17) has an effect on the observer like the faceted eyes of an insect with metallically gleaming lines of separation, almost in the way that bull's eye panes used to be enclosed and held together in traditional glass-making. Or are these parts of an air-filled container with a sculptural design? With the agates, all the organically active elements are continually bound in, enclosed and held by the wave-like form of the stone (18).

4 | **EYE CHALCEDONY** | MADAGASCAR
A landscape with agglomerations or the growth of microbes?

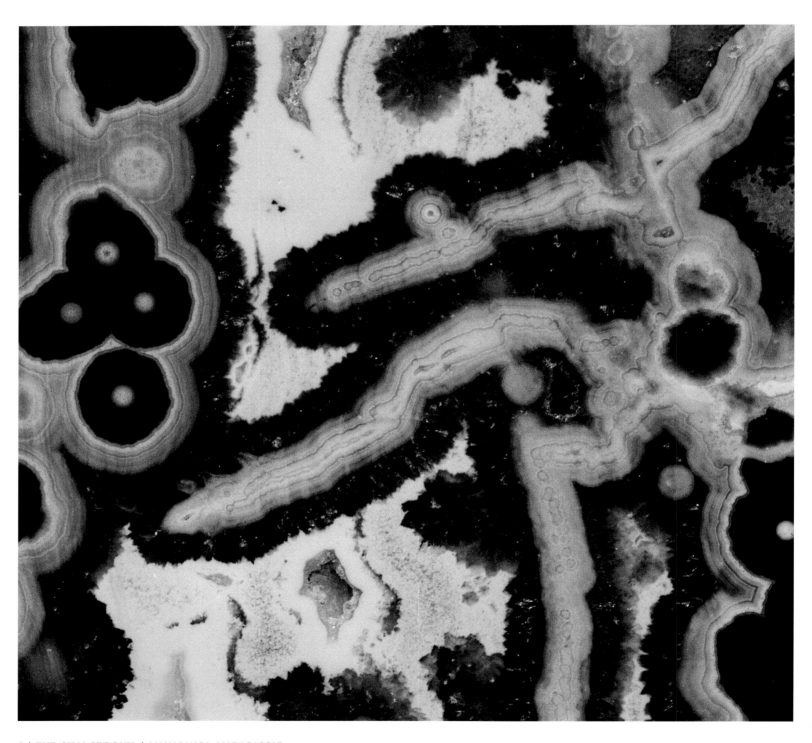

5 | **EYE CHALCEDONY** | MAHASANGA, MADAGASCAR
Rod bacteria and other micro-organisms seem to have
spread here.

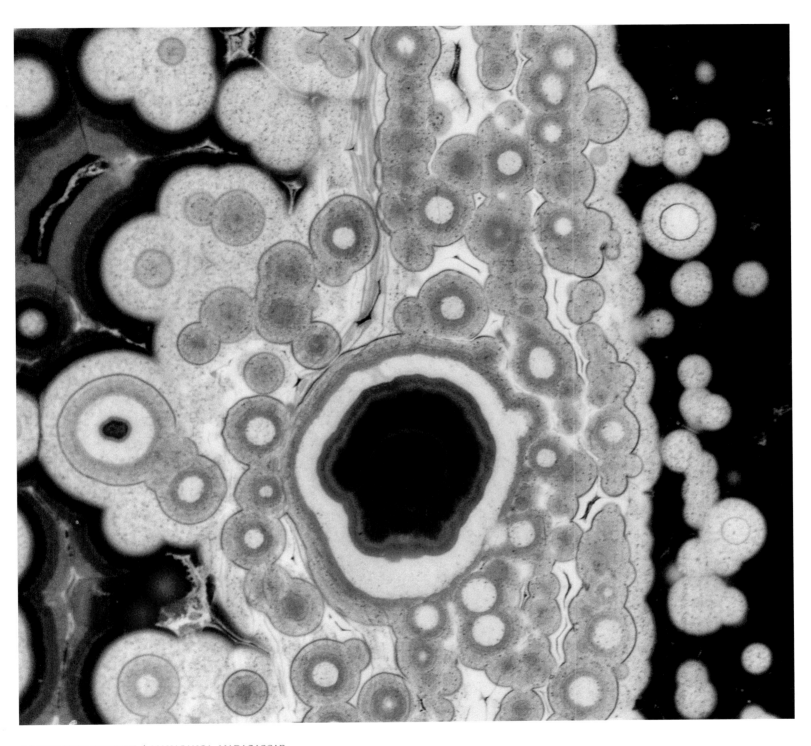

6 | **EYE CHALCEDONY** | MAHASANGA, MADAGASCAR
Black dots on a light background and bright dots on a
dark field.

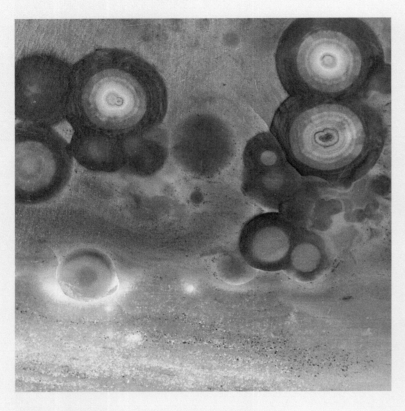

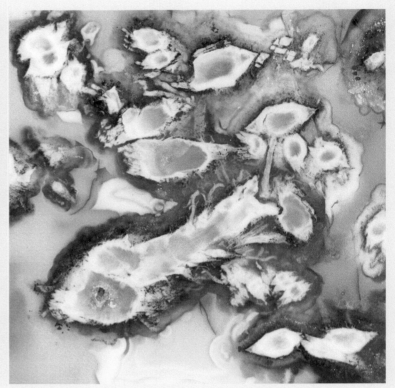

7 | **EYE CHALCEDONY** | MAHASANGA, MADAGASCAR
Dots and concentric circular formations on a diffused
background of pastel colours shine like the Milky Way in the
night sky.

8 | **AGATE** | SIDI RAHAL, MOROCCO
Small fish. Or plankton on the microscope slide?

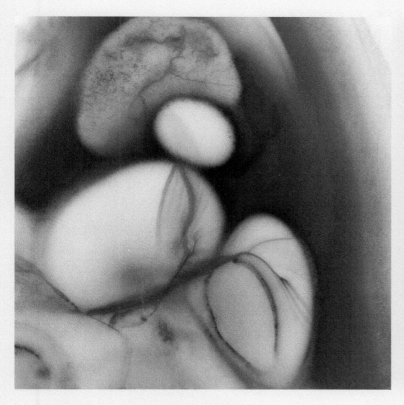

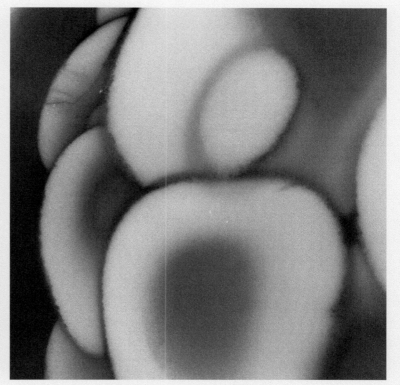

9 | **ORBICULAR JASPER** | ZACATECAS, MEXICO
Like ovoid organic formations nourished by blood vessels.

10 | **IMPERIAL JASPER** | CHIHUAHUA, MEXICO
Organic or inorganic? The graduated ovoid bodies guard
their secret.

11 | **EYE AGATE** | BRAZIL
The name of the stone says it all, but the look in the eye
is sombre.

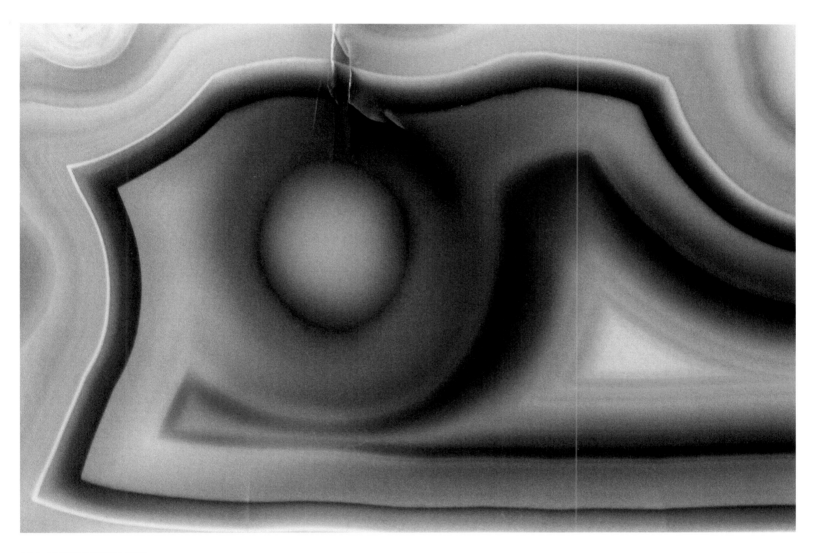

12 | **AGATE** | ZIMBABWE
This alternation of rounded and triangular forms is found in
many agates.

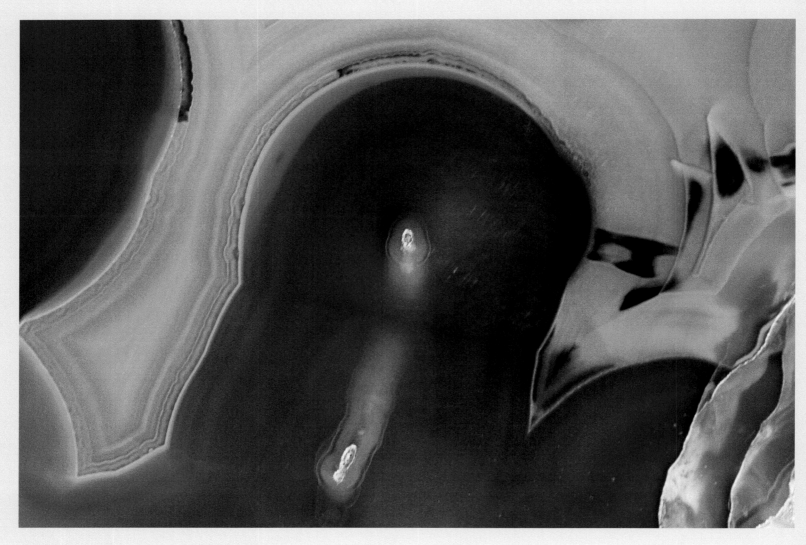

13 | **AGATE** | SAN RAFAEL, PATAGONIA, ARGENTINA
The dark, sombre mass seems to penetrate aggressively into
the bright red.

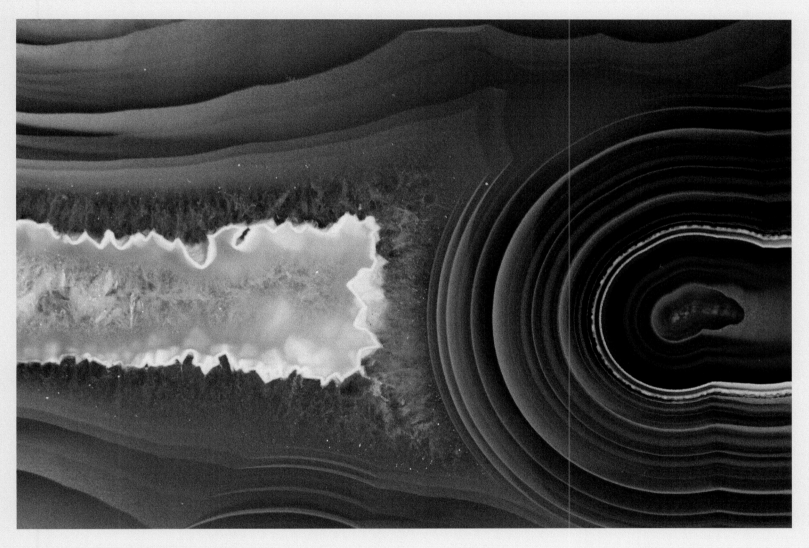

14 | **APAREJO AGATE** | CHIHUAHUA, MEXICO
The rounded dark part on the right seems to squeeze the
bright part together. On close examination there is an object
to be seen in the innermost of the dark curve that looks like
an insect larva.

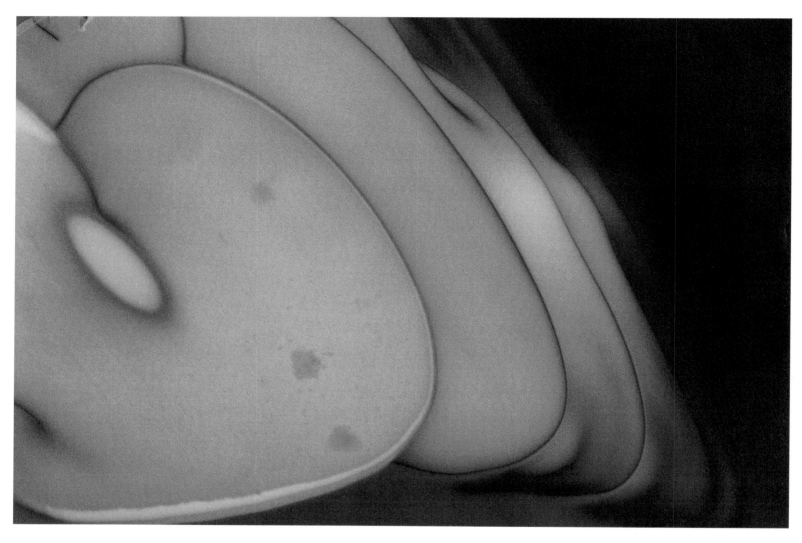

15 | **BRUNEAU JASPER** | BRUNEAU CANYON, IDAHO, USA
Mushroom-shaped organic formation.

16 | **BRUNEAU JASPER** | BRUNEAU CANYON, IDAHO, USA
Ovoid volumes crowd together or have grown together.

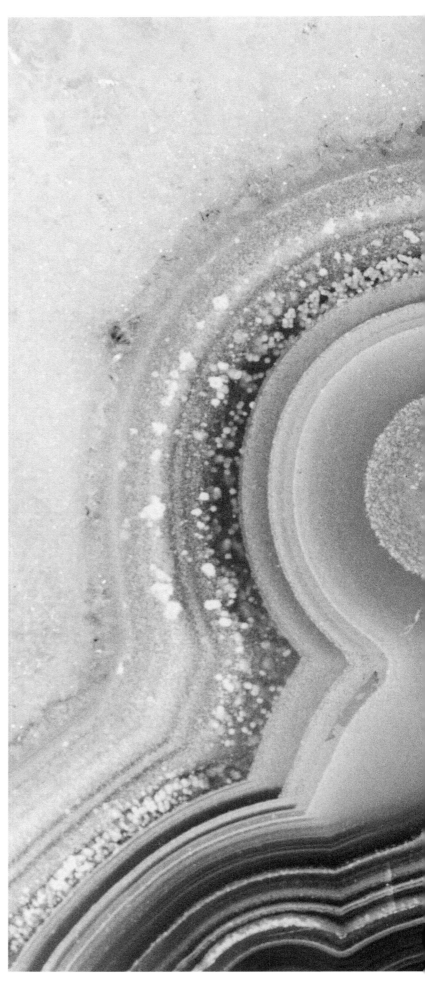

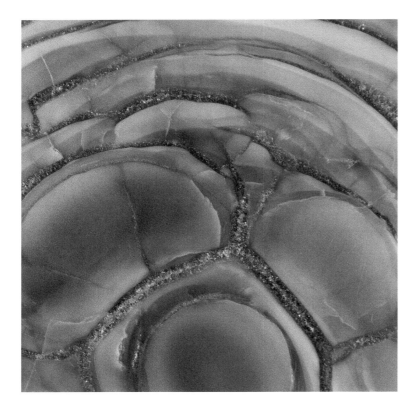

17 | **PETRIFIED WOOD** | YAKIMA RIVER VALLEY, WASHINGTON, USA
The eye of an insect, or great tents of synthetic material?

18 | **APAREJO AGATE** | CHIHUAHUA, MEXICO
From the strangely organic-looking dark forms in the lower centre of the image, forces seem to emanate, which in an increasing series of ripples finally create the great curve of the stone.

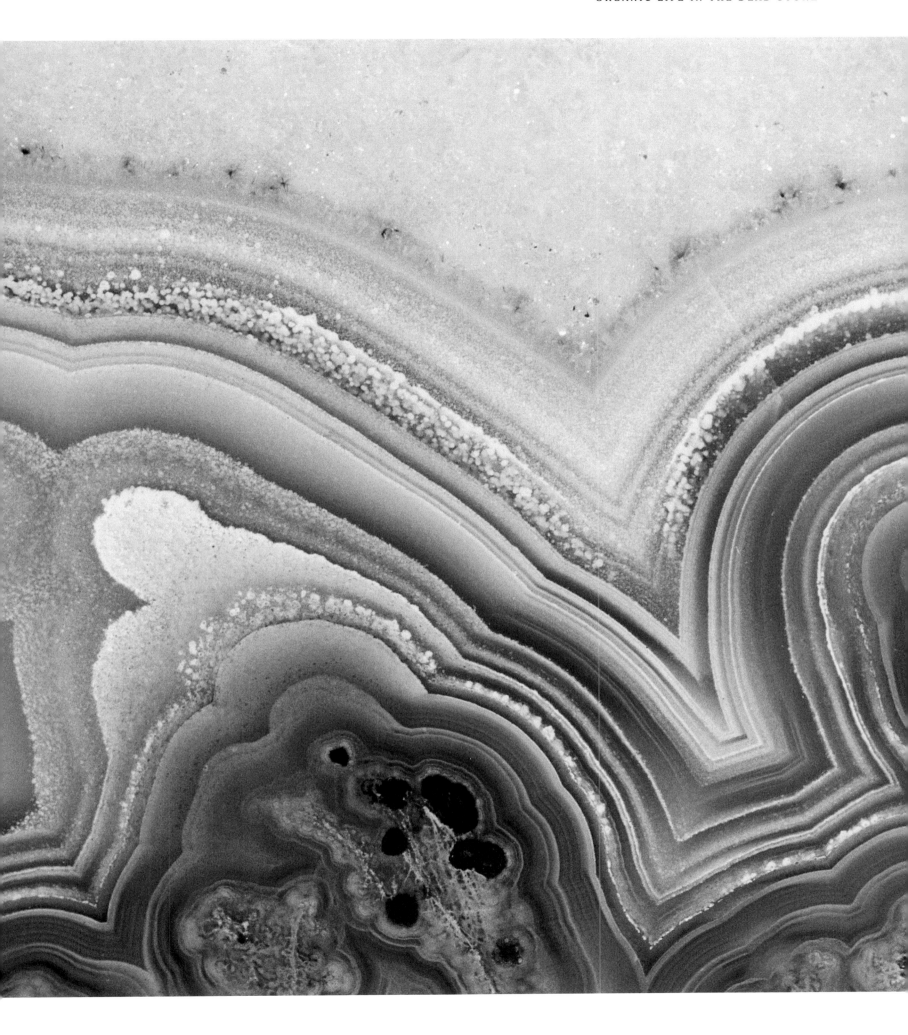

CRUSTY LICHENS AND SHIMMERING DENDRITES

19 | APAREJO AGATE | CHIHUAHUA, MEXICO
In the lower part of the image everything appears organic:
mosses and lichens have crept in. Are the porous openings
allowing material in, or is it flowing out? Above lies a vaulted
horizon in ever more geometrical layers.

Then crusty lichens (19, 20) suddenly grow across the image,
like cushions of moss, perhaps Icelandic moss; lichens such as
those we know from old trees in the mountains. How much
tension there is in these agates! These moving lines,
wonderfully arbitrary and yet clearly subject to a system,
partly white and partly dotted, separate areas from each
other, in which a totally different principle of growth seems
to rule: strangely amorphous green, brown and red lichens
flourish there – or algae. Algae are, after all, among the living
organisms that are part of lichens. Golden and silvery
dendrites on agates (21–24) are as decorative as jewellery on
expensive opaque glass.

20 | APAREJO AGATE | CHIHUAHUA, MEXICO
Here too, the contrast is striking between the crusty,
unstructured material and the elegantly drawn forms of
the agate.

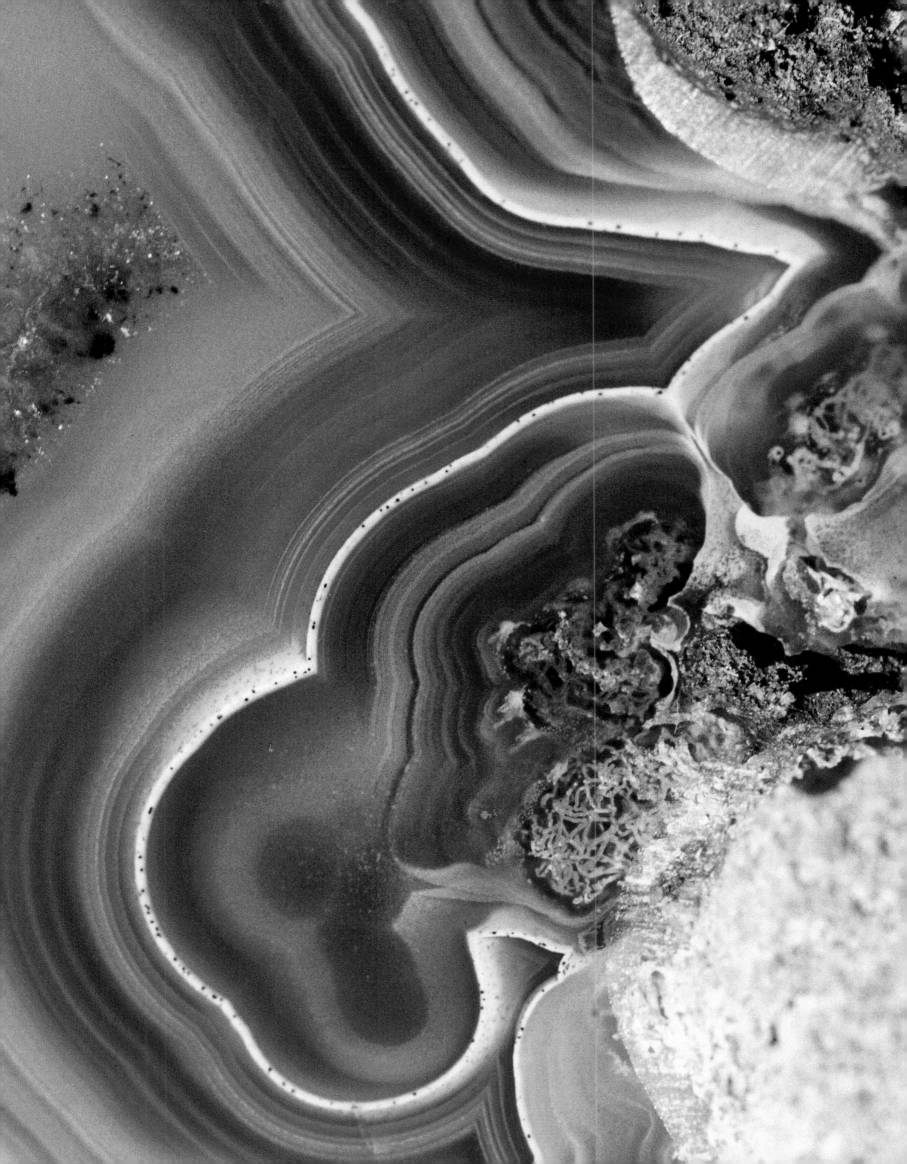

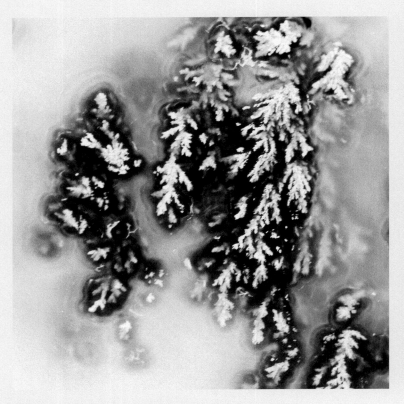

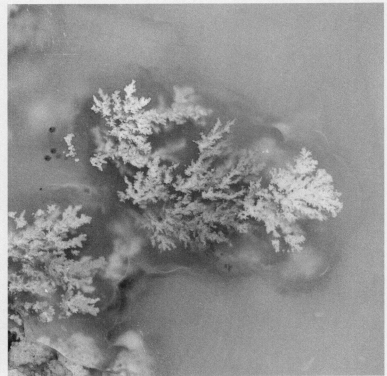

21 | **AGATE** | HORSE CANYON, TEHACHAPI, CALIFORNIA, USA
Dendritic branches grow through milky or blue chalcedony.

22 | **AGATE** | HORSE CANYON, TEHACHAPI, CALIFORNIA, USA
The contrast between milky-opaque stone and connecting
crystalline growths creates the impression of bushes or
water-plants.

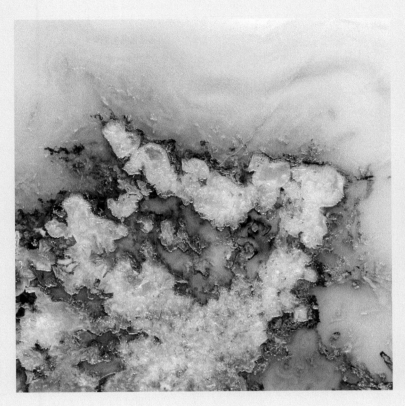

23 | **LAGUNA AGATE** | CHIHUAHUA, MEXICO
Delicate pastel tones of blue and pink offer a background for metallic-crystalline incrustations.

24 | **SNOW SCENE AGATE WITH DENDRITES** | OREGON, USA
Here too, we see a contrast between the soft pastel-coloured basic material and the metallic gleam of the dendrites growing into it.

ELEGANT BANDS

ELEGANT BANDS

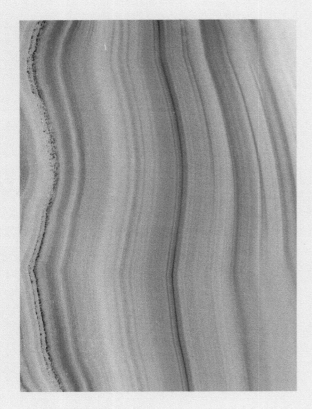

1 | AGATE | BRAZIL
The elegance of the gently moving band structures is one
characteristic of many agates, and the magical coloration is
another. The individual colours may be very clearly
demarcated from each other, and yet it seems as though
they are gently flowing into one another.

Opposite:
2 | AGATE | QUEENSLAND, AUSTRALIA
Here the spectrum flows from red to beige to orange,
without a single unattractive colour combination being
created. The transitions are smooth, and although the agate
has grown from outside to inside, one seems to be tricked by
the illusion that it is the innermost, primeval form that has
ultimately set the flow of all the lines in the right motion
with the rhythm of its form.

Here, it is the elegance of the banded structures and the
often very delicate colours that merge into one another that
arouse our enthusiasm (1). Fine gradations of colour with a
rhythm that comes into being from the constant repetition
of a motif that is never the same but always slightly varied, a
musical principle, or to put it rather more crudely, a bar code
from volcanic times. Sometimes the images not only gain in
depth as one seems to gaze into the semi-transparent stone,
but often seem to become sculptural. If the agate on pages
92-93 were a sawn-through tree stem, one could quickly
count up to 50 annual rings. As with the growth in width of
the tree, the conditions of the growth of this stone have not
always been the same. The dissolved minerals were not
always available in the same combination and numbers at
the same time. Thus elegant gradations of colour were
created, and a no less elegant, positively racy movement
allowed the agate to grow in a manner not concentrically
rounded, but sweepingly eccentric – it has a music of its own!
The agate with the oval red core has grown in a more regular
way (2). But that too has its energy; the innermost central line
seems to set the form and theme, and many variations can
be detected on the outside, even though the growth of the
stone presumably has taken the opposite route and in its
innermost core has finally found, as it were, the quintessence
of the form.

Another quality of agate is the alternation of clear lines,
drawn as though with Indian ink, with areas softly flowing
into each other, that seem drawn with pastel chalks (3, 4).
Much of it is runny, as though a gentle rain had washed the
colours away.

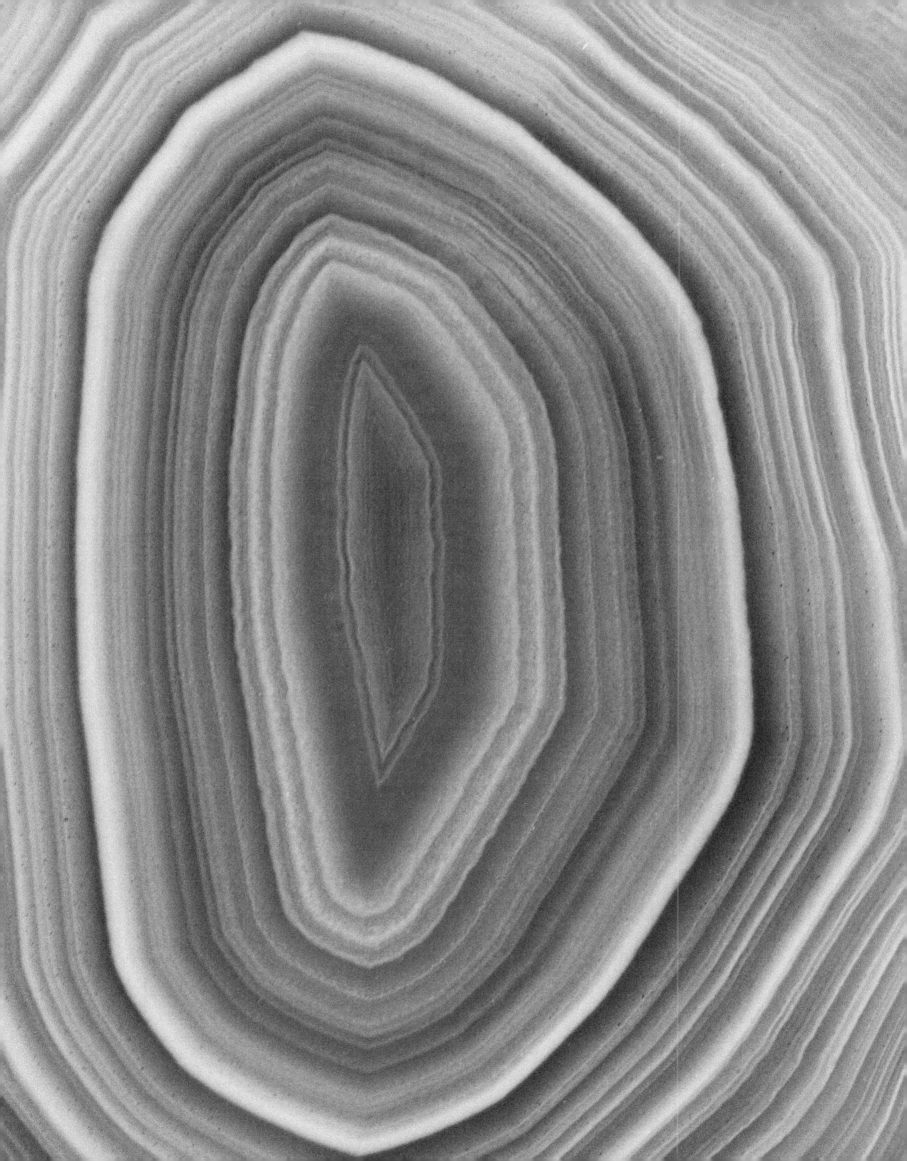

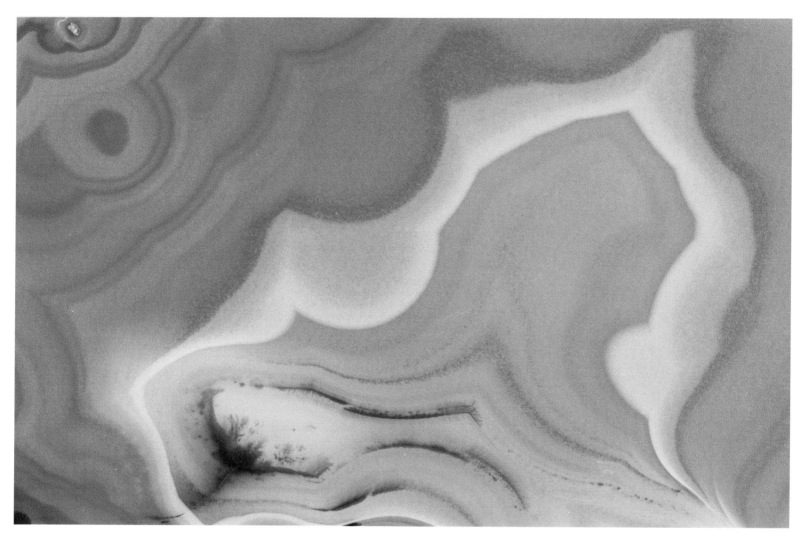

3 | **AGATE** | BRAZIL

Cloud-like waves of agate in delicate shades of yellow open
up, allowing a view into the depths, where ultimately, the
same process will take place – an imagined view into the
depths will again be offered. Because of the opaque or semi-
transparent properties of the material, the photograph
appears out of focus, but in reality, the view can only
penetrate so far into the material.

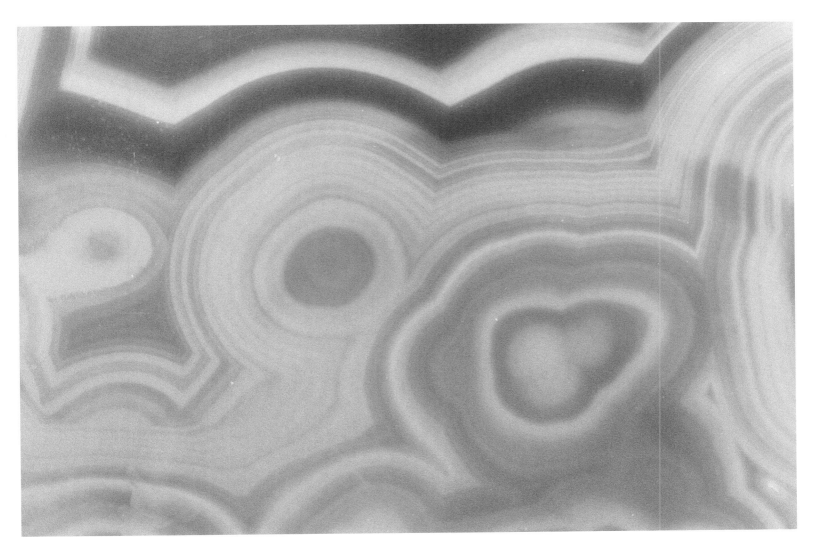

4 | **AGATE** | BRAZIL
This composition of shades of red and yellow, of rounded
and angular lines, gives us an impression of petrified music.
Many agates remind us of the techniques of the Art
Nouveau glass artists from Nancy, or of finely cut cameos.

A LOOK INTO THE KILN

5 | AGATE | SAN RAFAEL, PATAGONIA, ARGENTINA
This shot has a drama all of its own. It is as if one were
gazing at fiery heat in the oven, only – as with molten glass –
behind the thick broken discs of mica.

The range of the hard, clear lines of separation, like annual tree rings, through to the soft, merging transitions, is awesome. The soft merging, supported by the appropriate colours, makes us believe that the whole mass is still fluid, hot, in movement like fire and blazing flames in lively tones of red and orange that hurt our eyes when we look into a kiln in a glass factory (5). Just as well that the hot mass is once again curdling to a glassy, crystalline hardness, even if flames and streaming gases are still to be seen. Will a container now be created from the hot melt? A glass object that is being blown, of which we can see only the black opening (6)?

The wavy lines of the agate are particularly attractive when the fine transitions of colour are supplemented by a structure of fine dots (7, 8). In such cases, hardly anything can really be added to the variation of clear lines, gentle transitions and an astonishingly rich palette of colour. The agate's sequences of colour can also be enormously rich. It is like a bow of colour broken in several places – not in the colours of the rainbow, but in a sequence of black and brown through yellow and orange to violet, blue and finally carmine red (9). If you look closely, you can see a playful band of red that flouts the rules and flutters in a lively curve over the edge of the yellow spectrum.

6 | AGATE | RIO GRANDE DO SUL, BRAZIL
Spectacular shot of an agate in which deep black encounters shining cadmium yellow. There is great beauty not only in the multiple diffuse variation of the innermost, sharply outlined black 'basic theme', but also in the delicate opaline blue-green shimmer that is partly spread over the black.

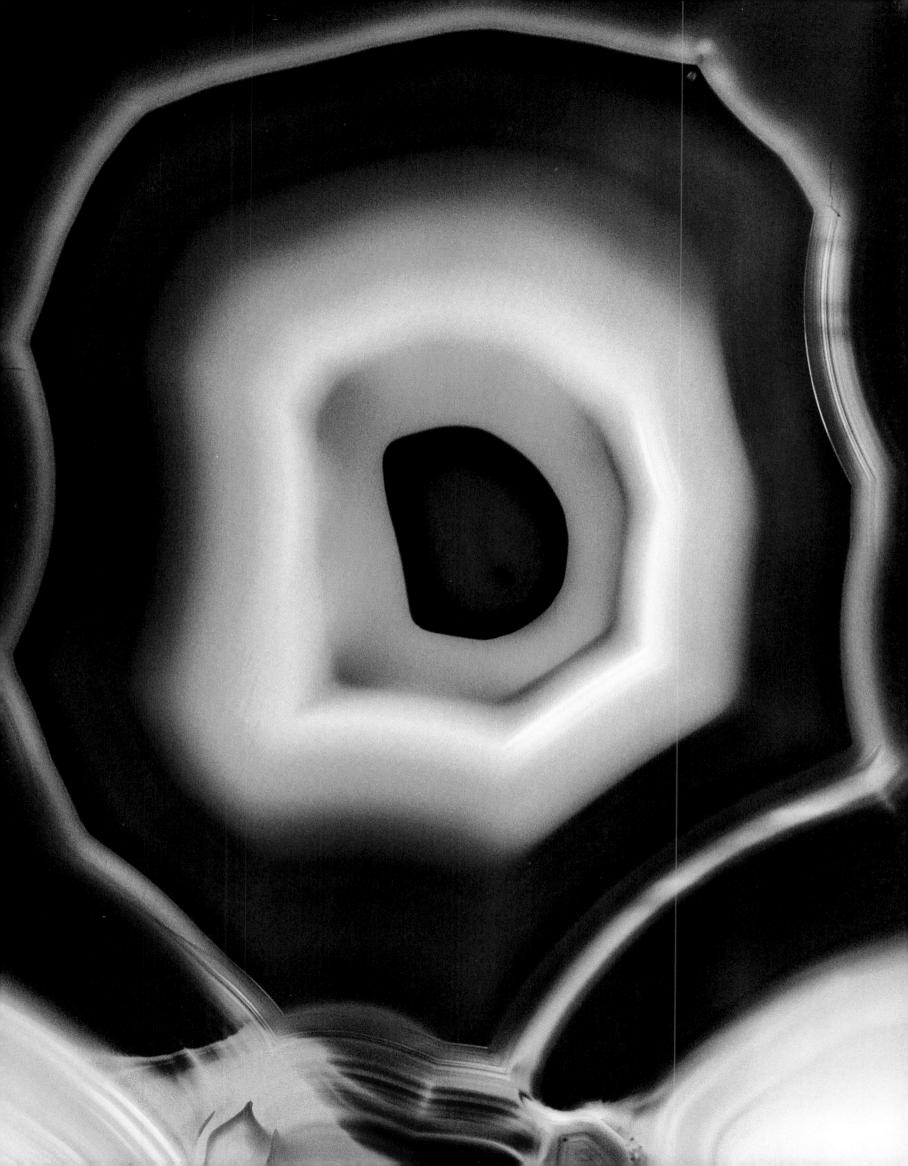

7 | **LAGUNA AGATE** | CHIHUAHUA, MEXICO
Lively curving lines with a superb variation of colour; the
'pointillist' red dots help the colours to flow harmoniously into
each other almost everywhere, with the exception of the
ivory-coloured line.

8 | **LAGUNA AGATE** | CHIHUAHUA, MEXICO
Colour and form have developed such a rhythm that it is
hard to believe that they have stayed motionless not only for
the split second of exposure, but for millions of years.

Following pages
9 | **LAGUNA AGATE** | CHIHUAHUA, MEXICO
A bow of colour – if not exactly a rainbow – is stretched over
a milky-white area of quartz. Particularly delightful is the
delicate red edge, subverting the system, in the lower part of
the bow.

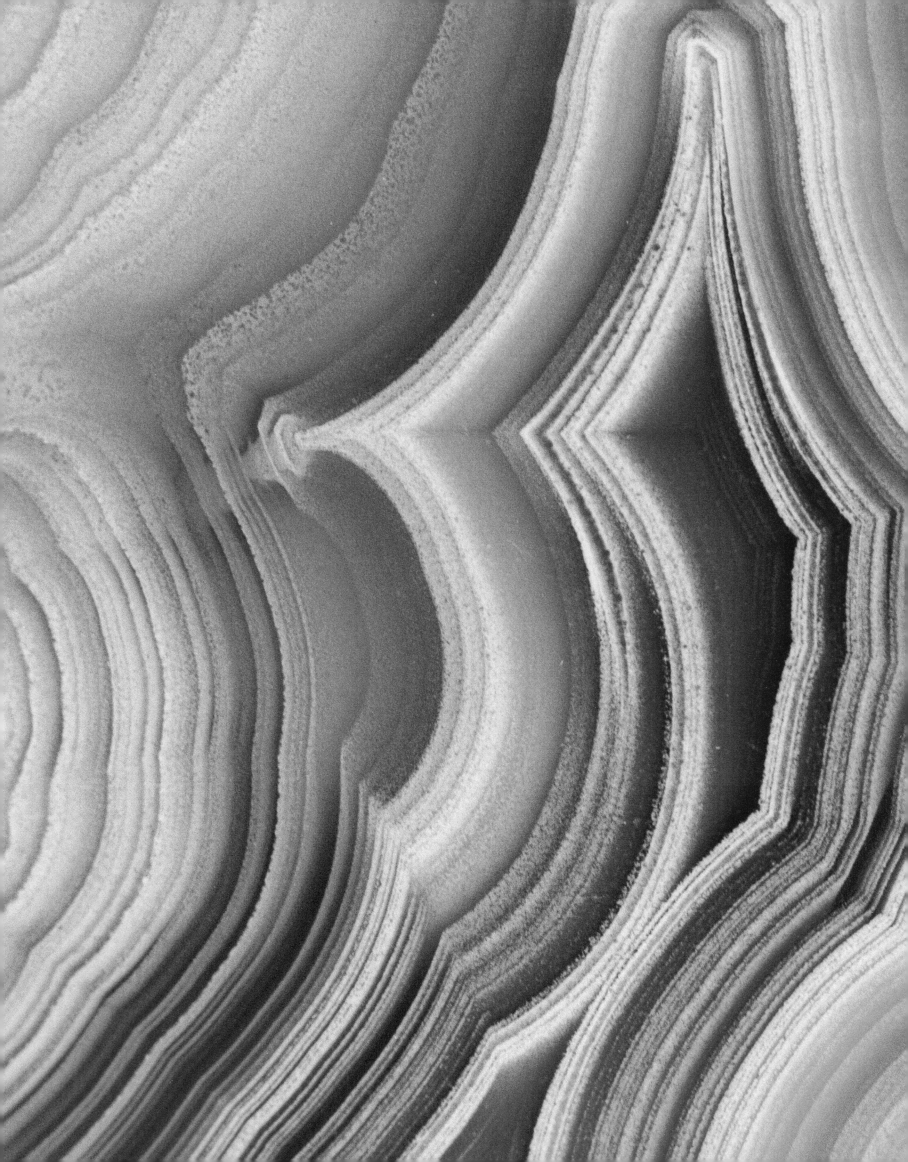

DECEPTIVE PLAY OF LIGHT AND SHADE

Let us stay for a moment with the agate and its wild play of waves. The harder and sharper the separations between the individual lines, the more sculptural is the impression given by the agates. The eye interprets shadings as the result of an intrusion of light and the casting of a shadow. For this reason the bands of the agate often appear to be positioned (10, 11), like folded, bundled strips of paper. Particularly effective are the shots in which these well-ordered, sharp-edged bands encounter zones of flatter, less well-defined material. One can only admire the mutual penetration of forms and colours, of bright light and opaque, faint two-dimensionality (11). From established grey structures, which, wave by wave, curve more and more against a peak, a brilliantly brightening stream breaks into the red mass. Or is it the exact opposite – that the red mass pushes its way into the grey, with the concentrated force of a rounded curve, and dissolves and destroys its delicate structures? We do not know, but for us the rigid frontier line is the final record, which holds fast the definitive stage of this blended mass.

The light-coloured parts resemble folded-up, starched and ironed pleated collars (12), while the red areas of the agate, which crowd between these structures, give a chaotic or amorphous impression. Has a confectioner carefully wrapped his product first in a lacy-edged paper and then in several layers of card? With agates one never knows which part is the wrapping and which the wrapped – both appear in both roles. If the eye loses itself in these pleated labyrinths, suddenly the outside can become the inside and the inside the outside, as with M.C. Escher's trompe l'oeil drawings (13). Here we are looking into broken tubes, into deep furrows and embedded structures as with paper boats folded in complicated ways or artfully arranged table napkins (14). And yet the stone is polished completely flat; this is all a deception of the eye, evoked by the supposed play of light and shade.

10 | **LAGUNA AGATE** | CHIHUAHUA, MEXICO
A play of colours and forms with an effect of incredible depth. It is exciting to see how the spur breaking out to the left seems to bore into the neighbouring bands of agate.

11 | **APAREJO AGATE** | CHIHUAHUA, MEXICO
In the dramatic lighting of a surrealist picture, the developing
masses penetrate each other.

12 | **APAREJO AGATE** | CHIHUAHUA, MEXICO
The polished surface here becomes a three-dimensional space.
The forms are draped like paper backdrops. Knife-sharp, severe
contours alternate with playful, cheekily ornate areas.

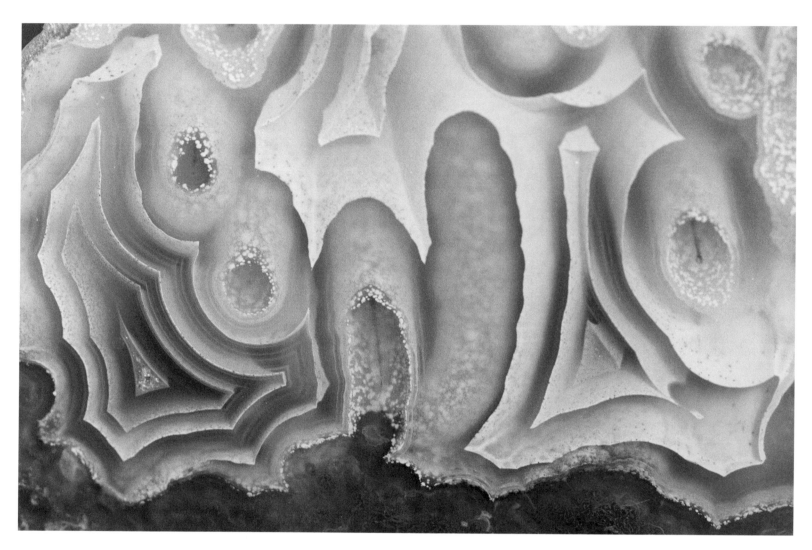

13 | **APAREJO AGATE** | CHIHUAHUA, MEXICO
Here, too, sharply outlined contours alternate with
strangely tubular formations, which are partly cut open,
allowing a view inside them. Yet the eye can lose its way
and be deceived in this labyrinth.

14 | **LAGUNA AGATE** | CHIHUAHUA, MEXICO

These elegantly curving lines are like folded paper. Each band of the agate runs parallel, but not in quite the same way as the others. This provides the rhythm, the 'music' of the image.

BATTLE ZONES

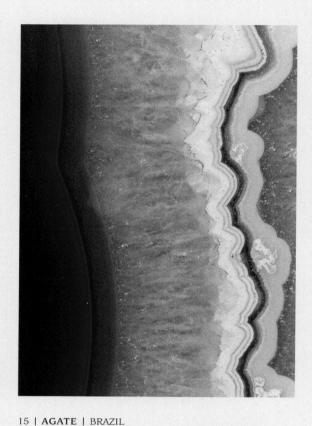

15 | AGATE | BRAZIL
Macrocrystalline and microcrystalline areas alternate with each other, and the tallest jagged peaks of the quartz crystal (rock crystal) are relieved by lines which, gathering all together, copy the to-and-fro of the crystals. They flow into an olive-coloured band, which itself borders on a light blue one, which, with its gentle curves, in a heightened calligraphy, allows the rhythm set by the crystals to run its course.

On close examination, it is seen that often macrocrystalline – and thus transparent – geometrically clearly outlined crystallizations are carrying on a wild battle of displacement with microcrystalline wave-shaped structures in which feathers can fly (17). Rock crystals (15, 16) can set agate structures in motion from two sides. The crystals are like a mountain range with pointed peaks, overarched by the ever more gently rounded lines, which probably copy to some extent the form that this massif will take after millennia of erosion. In the centre of the symmetrically arranged areas of pressure there is a clearly visible break in the glassy crystal, which marks the line of separation of these battle zones. The movement set off by the crystals subsides into the straight-lined band structure of the agate only after a multitude of lines (18). Often it is precisely this area, where the crystals have grown together from both sides, that is one of the most interesting and striking (19). A glance at these areas of crystallization shows how closely interconnected this measuring of powers can be when it comes to a halt (20). Often this macrocrystalline area does not close up completely, but leaves just one opening free (21).

16 | AGATE | BRAZIL
A larger section of the agate opposite. It can be seen that the system described above is to be observed from two sides. In the centre is an area, again macrocrystalline and therefore transparent (with shining crystallization areas), which has grown together with the opposite area along a fracture line. In this way the opening in the inside of the geode has finally completely closed.

Following pages:
17 | LAGUNA AGATE | CHIHUAHUA, MEXICO
A wonderful play of macrocrystalline transparent quartz with blazing surfaces of crystallization, and microcrystalline grey or white agate.

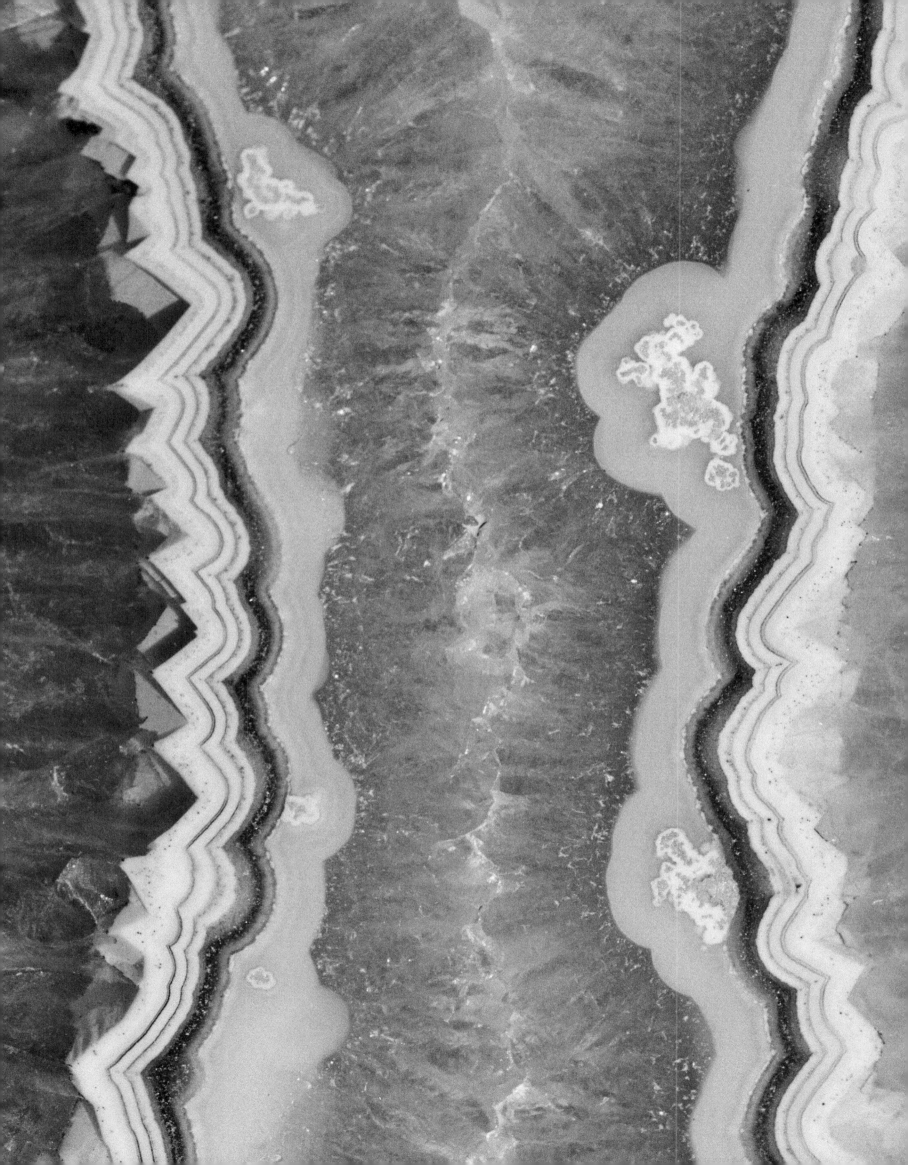

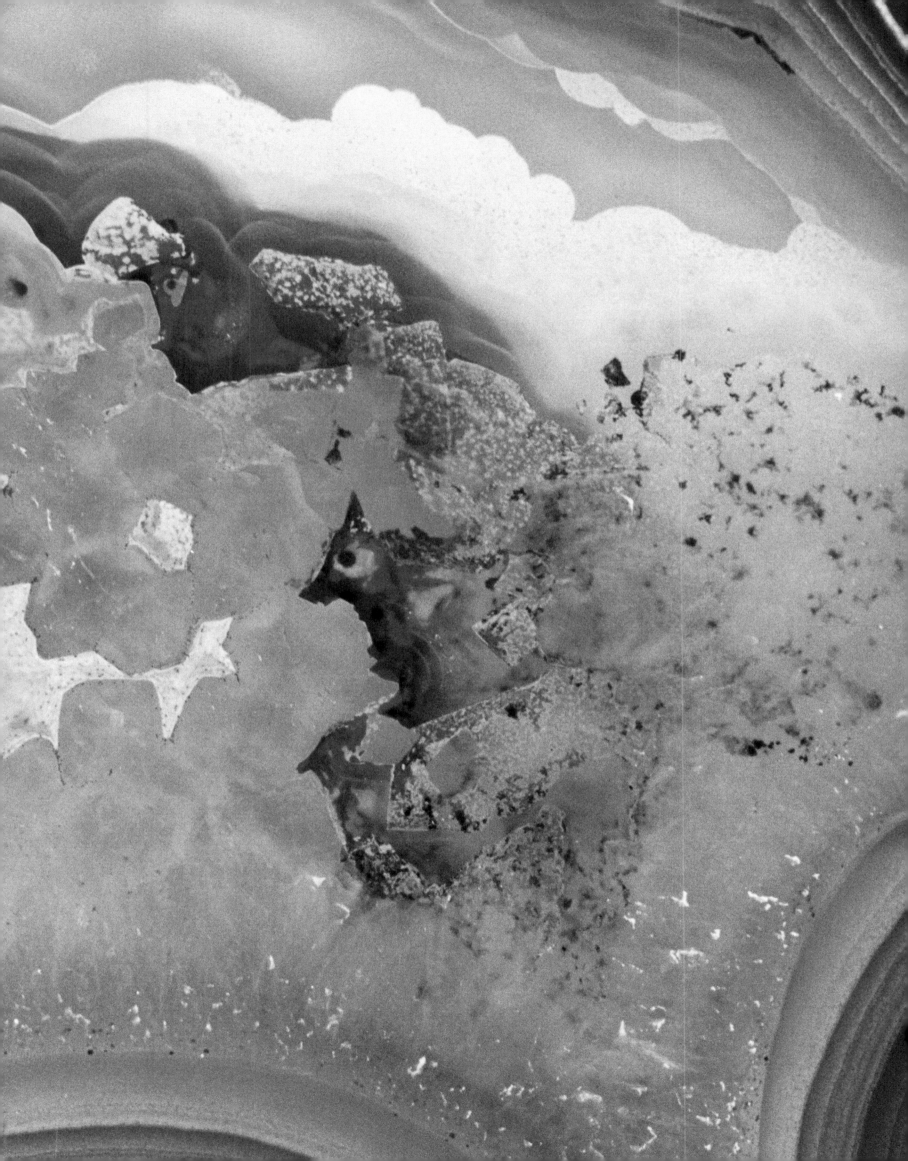

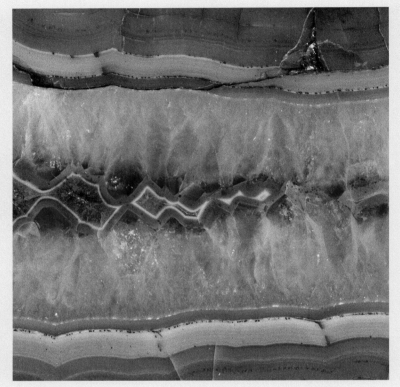

18 | **AGATE** | BRAZIL
Again the transition from (grey) crystallized quartz to the
microcrystalline agate lines sets the rhythm of this image. In
terms of colour, the gradation of various shades of grey and yellow
is also very attractive.

19 | **AGATE** | OBERBROMBACH, IDAR-OBERSTEIN, GERMANY
Before the crystallizing mass of quartz (which is enclosed on both
sides by a more or less symmetrically built-up opaque, reddish-
green agate surface) could unite in the centre, a glowing orange
layer of agate has formed once again.

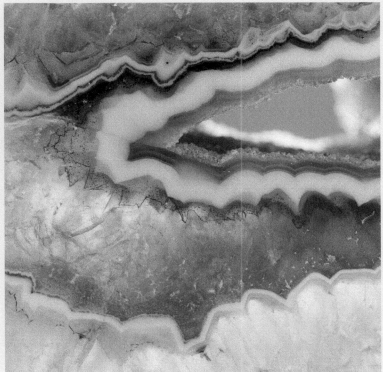

20 | **AGATE** | BRAZIL
Crystalline front in the innermost part of an agate. The quartz
crystals have the effect of biting teeth.

21 | **AGATE** | BRAZIL
The backlighting here shows up the varying translucency of
crystalline and opaque areas in the agate, which alternate in a rapid
rhythm. The innermost area of the geode has stayed open, and one
sees the fine serrated edge of rock crystals, which were the last to
grow before the supply of material was apparently broken off.

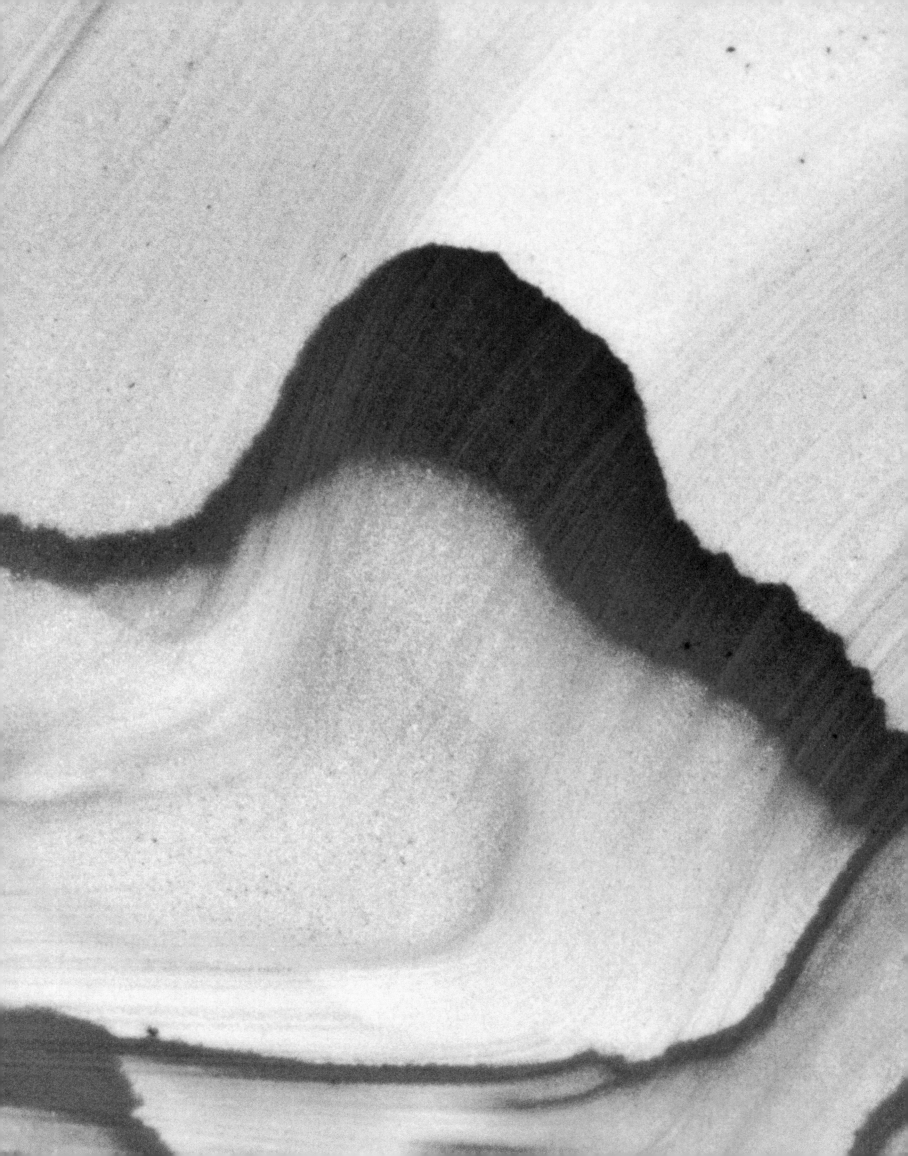

LANDSCAPE IMAGES

LANDSCAPE IMAGES

We have already spoken of mountains and similar geographical formations in connection with agates. This relationship is even more marked with marble and other sedimentary rocks. Apart from the associations with microscopically small biological objects, many stones awaken in us the vision of a great, spacious landscape. Echelons of hill areas and sandy, stratified desert landscapes can be seen in the superb Kanab Golden Stone (1, 2). We find the same sweep in the Owyhee Jasper (previous pages) and in the Biggs Jasper from Oregon (3), the second of which reproduces a dramatically lively landscape, often to be read like bodily forms: a baroque crumpled landscape with hard shadows, which created an astonishingly sculptural effect.

1 | **KANAB GOLDEN STONE** | KANAB, UTAH, USA
Splendidly patterned landscape with sandy structures, which seems to show the strata of the rock.

2 | **KANAB GOLDEN STONE** | KANAB, UTAH, USA
Mountain landscape in staggered sections, with clear contours, between them valleys giving an impression of depth. In the foreground, a lake seems to lie in front of a sandy plain.

Following pages:
3 | **BIGGS JASPER** | OREGON, USA
This jasper shows a wild landscape full of movement, which looks in certain areas as though laced in. Here, too, the strong contours, the rounded forms and the variable 'lighting' of the 'hills' and 'mountains' have a dramatic effect.

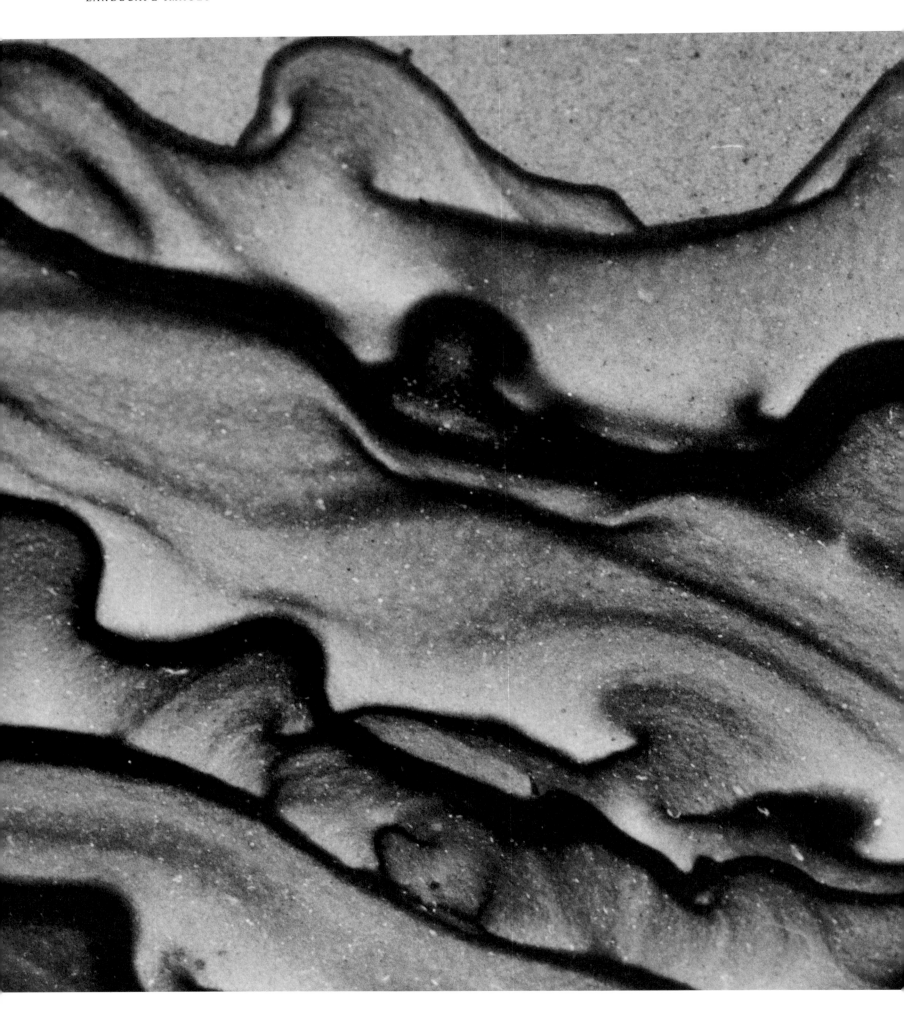

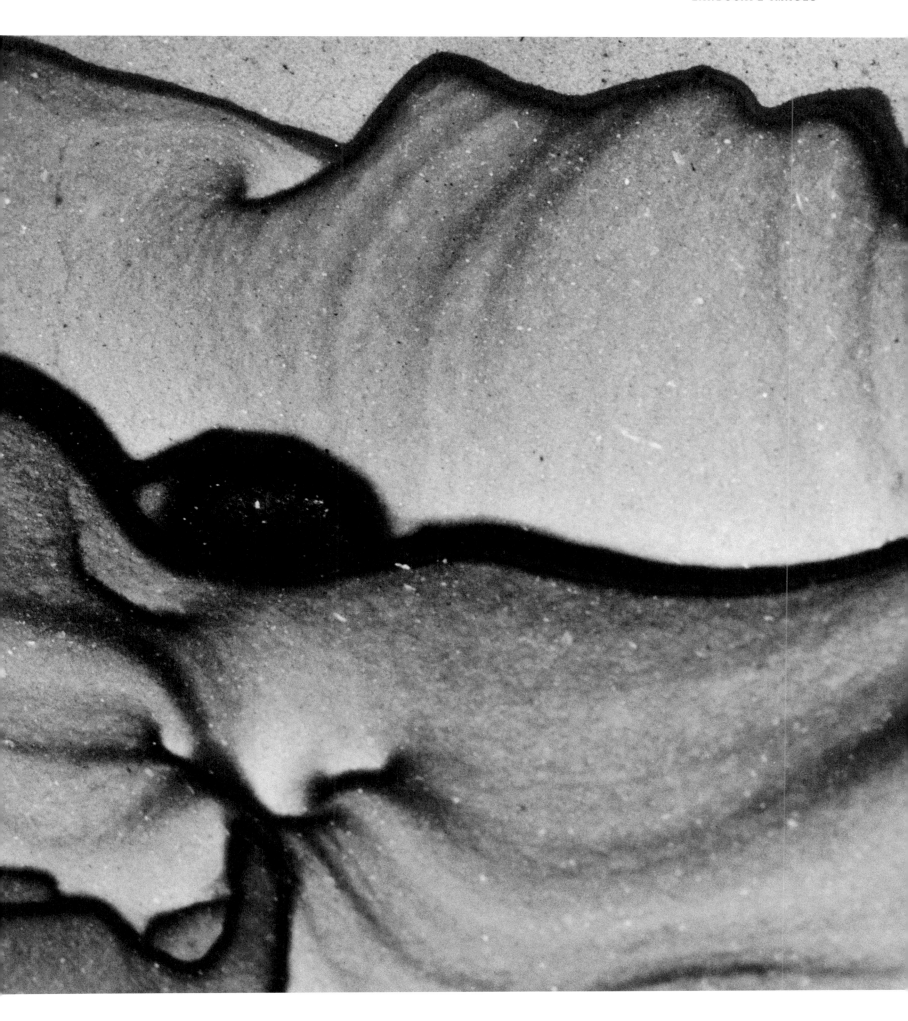

TECTONICS IN POCKET SIZE

4 | LANDSCAPE MARBLE | PAESINA, FLORENCE, ITALY
Like the previous examples, the stone probably once showed
strongly contoured, gently flowing landscapes with
noticeable layers. Then, tectonic forces created fractures and
shifts – as indeed happens with Alpine folds and the
development of other mountain ranges.

Much more rigid, and traversed by many fracture lines, is the
landscape marble from Tuscany (4, 5); but this landscape is
also full of a wild theatricality. Erosion has rounded off the
rock formations; old fracture areas are overlaid by new ones,
which push aside the old cracks in a parallel movement.
These images show us, as it were in miniature format, the
tectonic folds and fractures of our mountain ranges (6–9), for
it is precisely these forces that have formed the stone plates
reproduced here.

Here, too, nature records on a small scale what happens on
a large one. Geologically, this series is probably among the
most interesting in this book, for here one experiences the
mighty physical processes of plate tectonics, mountain folds
and rift valleys in miniature, and the layers of rock allow us to
reconstruct the appearance of the structures before these
forces set in. What makes the images even more valuable is
that dendrites also create the illusion of vegetation, which
enlivens this rocky landscape, and simulates a real
mountainous setting. A variscite from the USA (10) shows a
boldly painted landscape, which can be seen from afar, linked
with the vigorous peaks of the Matterhorn.

5 | LANDSCAPE MARBLE | PAESINA, FLORENCE, ITALY
In this landscape marble, the fracture lines have such a
dominant effect that one is reminded of the generally
regular rock bands of a mountain landscape or a large
quarry, where roads laid out as ramps give access to the
individual quarrying sites.

6 | **LANDSCAPE MARBLE** | PAESINA, FLORENCE, ITALY
This jagged rocky landscape is filled with additional life by
aspiring dendrites, reminiscent of plants: lichens or even
tufts of grass or bushes have conquered the stony massif.

7 | **LANDSCAPE MARBLE** | PAESINA, FLORENCE, ITALY
A landscape like a stage set, partly built up from cubist
forms.

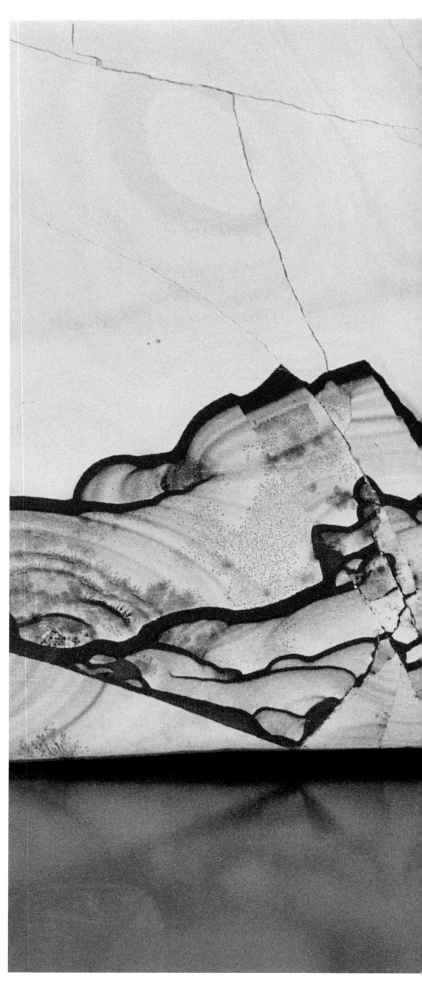

8 | **LANDSCAPE MARBLE** | PAESINA, FLORENCE, ITALY
A little Monument Valley – rocks left over from an otherwise largely eroded mountain range? A landscape like one from a surrealist painting.

9 | **LANDSCAPE MARBLE** | PAESINA, FLORENCE, ITALY
A little history of geology: the same tectonic forces that allow mountain ranges to rise up also formed this 'landscape marble'.

Following pages:
10 | **VARISCITE** | FAIRFIELD, UTAH, USA
This is how an artist of our own time might experience and reproduce the scenery of a mighty mountain backdrop.

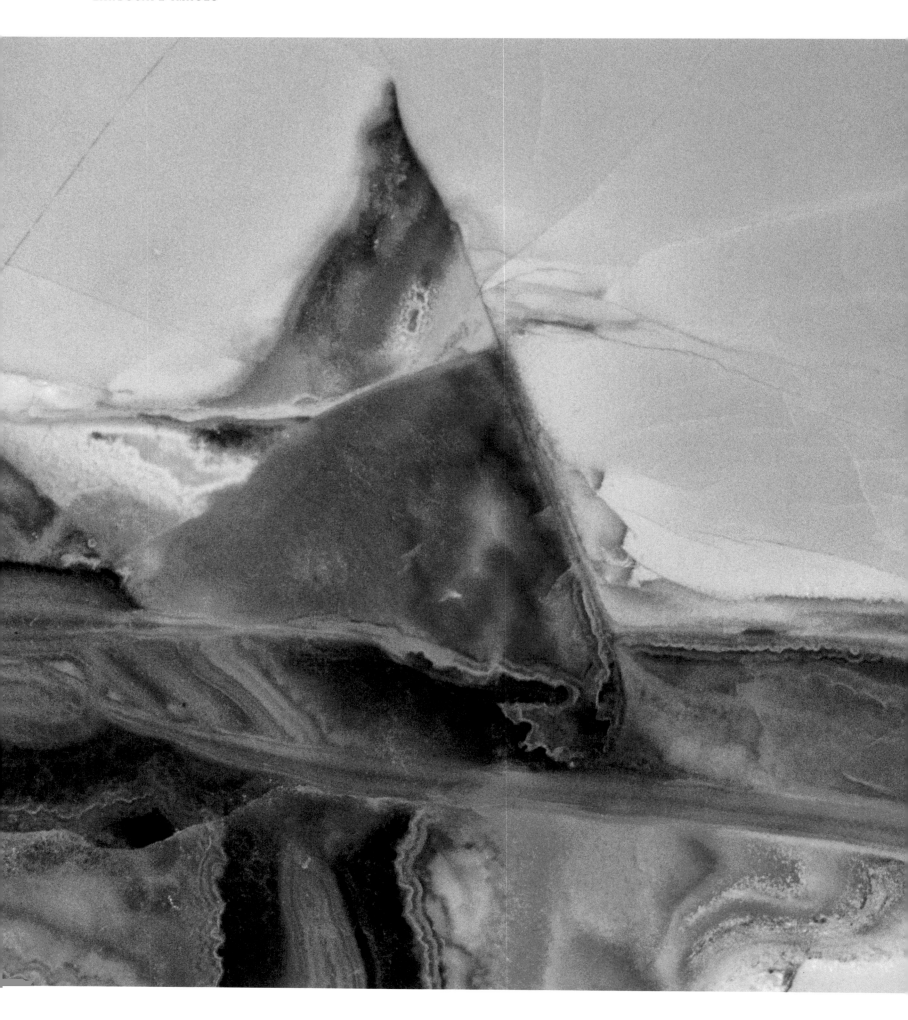

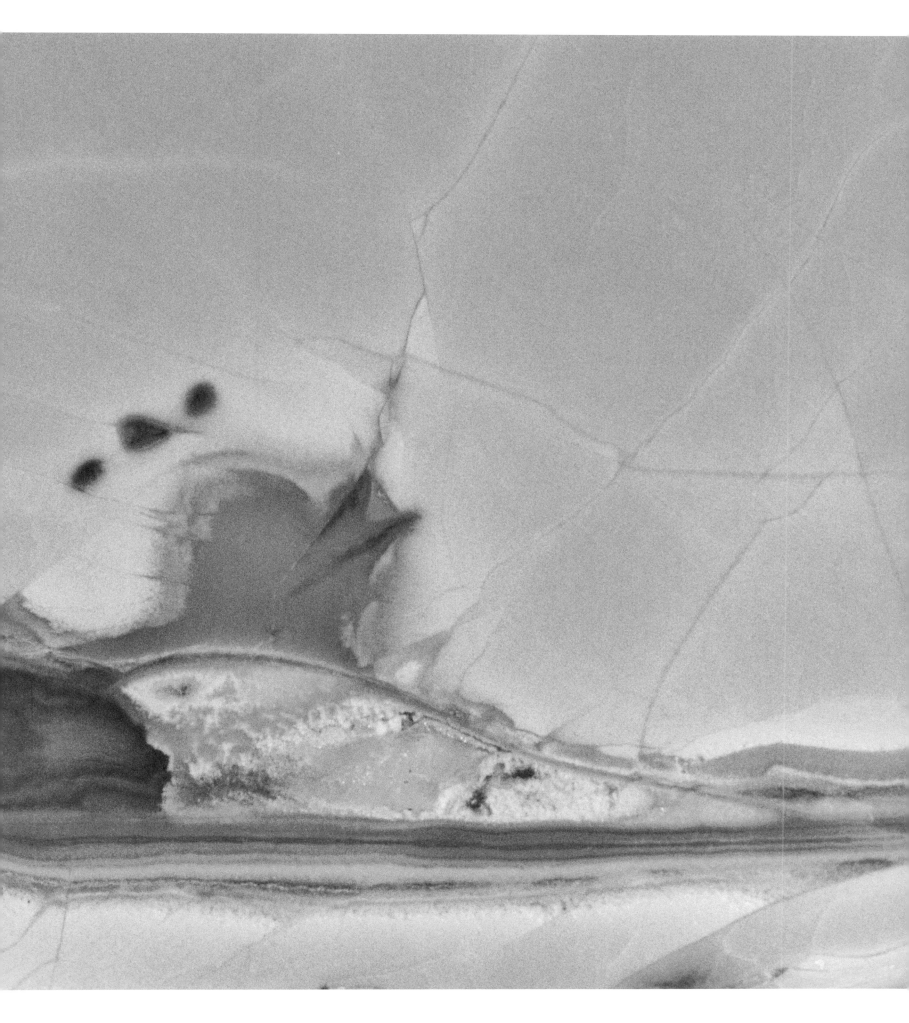

OPERA STAGES AND DELICATE WATERCOLOURS

A further highlight of this book is a series of dramatic photographs, really very artistic in appearance, of Brazilian geodes: stupendous imaginary landscapes can be seen in these agates from Soledade (11, 12), which – with their powerful, mostly translucent colours that look like watercolours – excite our imaginations. Are these images from a visionary underworld, a contemporary opera production, a film set in other worlds? Or has this landscape long been liquid, hot glass, which sprays out of a furnace? Or can we even recognize enormously enlarged faces, which rear up, but soon pass away again in the glowing mass?

The honey-coloured formations remind us of amber, a warm organic material, in which one often finds little insects that have been enclosed for millions of years in the rigid, transparent mass. Dendrites on chalcedony (13) resemble a winter landscape at sunset, when long shadows fall upon the snow. A Japanese painter with his bold but fine brush-strokes could have captured such a scene: a broad melancholic landscape with only a row of bushes or trees rising up, whose shadows move like a reflection over the surface.

11 | **AGATE** | SOLEDADE, RIO GRANDE DO SUL, BRAZIL
This dramatic view does not perhaps conjure up at first sight a landscape. One might see in it a head with a dog's snout, or an overhanging rock.

12 | **AGATE** | SOLEDADE, RIO GRANDE DO SUL, BRAZIL
The transparency and the dark colours make this landscape
look like a dream landscape; it is overlaid by a certain magic,
as when we experience a solar eclipse.

13 | DENDRITE CHALCEDONY | BRAZIL
A sunrise or sunset in a wintry landscape, captured by the
fine watercolour brush, extends before our eyes.

INNER WORLDS IN THE INMOST PART OF STONES

14 | AGATE | BRAZIL
As if brought elegantly onto paper with an ink brush, this opaque agate allows the eye to penetrate to some extent into the depth of the material. It is an effect similar to that of a watercolour, where the colours are absorbed by the paper and flow slightly into each other, creating a fluffy blur.

Less dramatic, but no less lively and artistic are the agates from Brazil (14, 15), which really do belong in the realm of painting: watercolours lightly applied with a calligraphic sweep by a Japanese brush, or dabbed with a pointed brush; merging colours, veils that invite a dive into a bright, lively world which resists concrete interpretation. Landscapes finely painted in watercolour can also be seen in further images from a series of Brazilian agates (16–19) that show striking contours and very delicate sequences of colours. Blue, yellow and red – always with a super-fine lightness reminiscent of glass paintings – form a dune or winter landscape. They are bounded by a row of crystals, which form, according to how one sees it, either a base or, when one turns the image, a jagged mountain range at the top, above which floats a glassy sky. Two other agates in this series (18, 20) are a vortex captured in the image, a gust of wind perhaps, that drives a few leaves along past our eyes, a look into a kaleidoscope, or into the hidden inner part of the stones, where 'le paysage de l'âme' (the landscape of the heart) is spread out.

15 | AGATE | BRAZIL
The super-fine colours running their course cannot disguise the fact that this is an agate that has come into being according to the same principles as all the others in this book. If you have so far been carefully observing these agates, you will at once recognize the white lines, below right, and how the second, finer blue bow runs parallel to the first, like a faint, second rainbow.

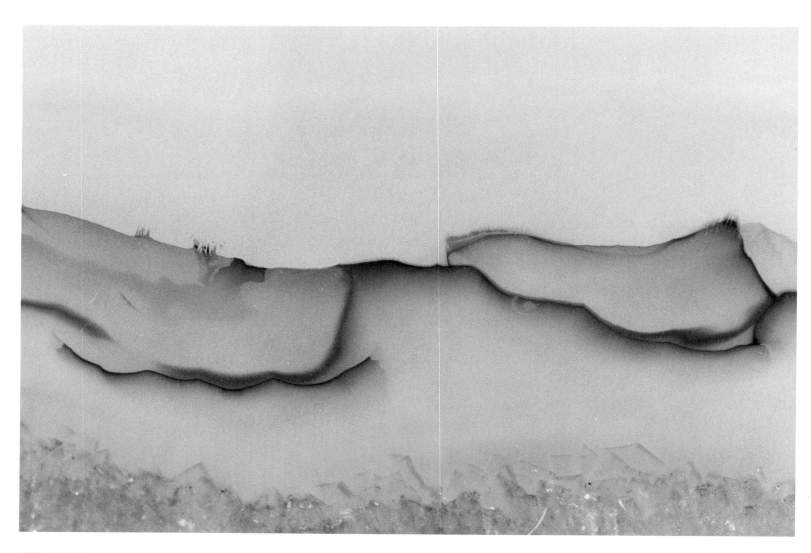

16 | **AGATE** | SOLEDADE, RIO GRANDE DO SUL, BRAZIL
A very attractive play of colours and forms, with pastel
shades flowing gently into each other. Can we still see a
landscape in it, or what appears to be abstract art, with clear
contours and gently flowing colours in between? Let us leave
it at a landscape, dunes with coloured sand, accentuated by
the occasional tuft of grass.

17 | **AGATE** | SOLEDADE, RIO GRANDE DO SUL, BRAZIL
A winter landscape with the background wreathed in fog or
the snow being blown by the wind? Here and also in the
picture on the left, one sees at the base another series of
transparent, crystallized quartz crystals, whose surfaces are
partly lit up by the sunlight. Their peaks are as though
poured into the fine-grained, microcrystalline agate material.

Following pages:
18 | **AGATE** | BRAZIL
Here too, an artist appears to have been at work. Everything
seems to be going through a process of dissolution,
everything is in motion: one seems to discern birds and
leaves carried along by the storm.

19 | **AGATE** | BRAZIL
An artistically designed 'landscape'. In the foreground we
still seem to see mountain-sides and rocks, but otherwise
the landscape melts away in the glowing red sky.

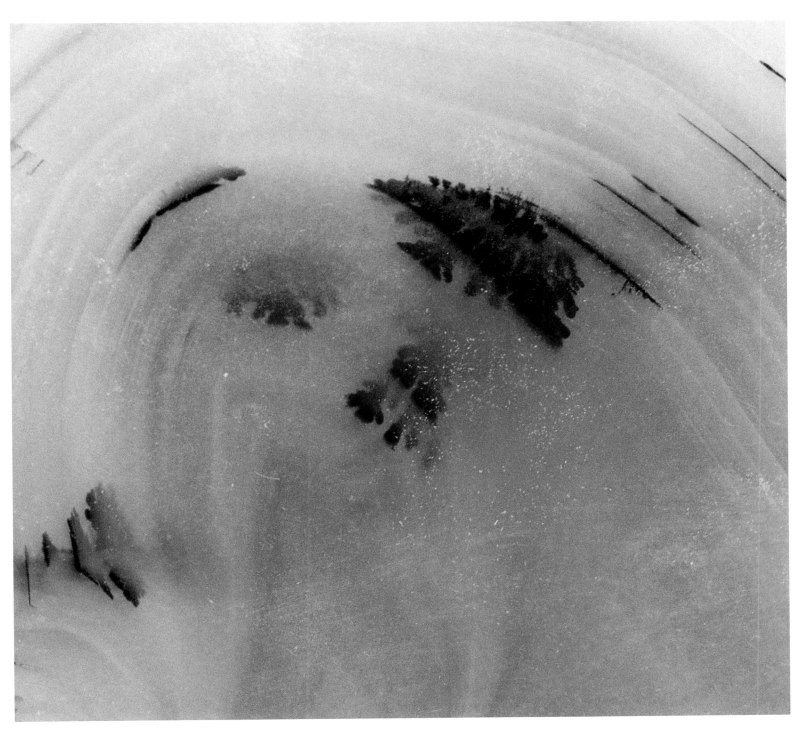

20 | **LAGUNA AGATE** | CHIHUAHUA, MEXICO
A certain transparency allows us to see behind the surface of
these stones. Here too, one has the impression of a
whirlwind, a movement that carries much along with it.

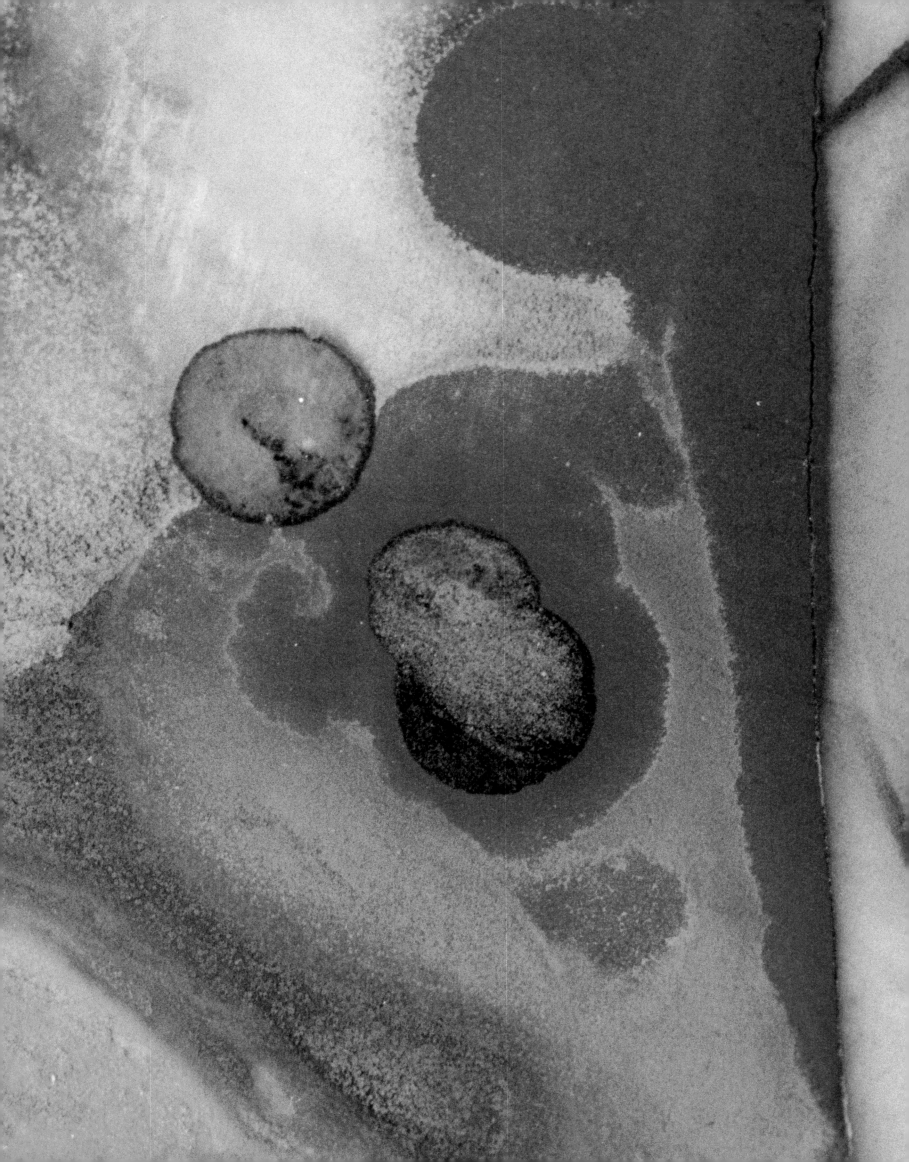

ASSOCIATIONS AND VISIONS

SOLIDIFIED

1 | BRECCIA WITH QUARTZ | USA
A stone which is actually a collection of stones. Broken and also slightly rounded sand gravel has become bound in quartz. The individual stones have different origins and have been accidentally brought together by the glacier, stream or river. Nevertheless, the image appears as though specially designed.

An extreme opposite pole to the gently flowing, watercolour-like forms is represented by a series of objects that seems to project harshly into the space, and that proves that geology has other means for the mingling of materials than just gentle growing together and melting and dissolving into each other. This series includes strange collections of forms, such as 'paints' jasper from Oregon, USA, lying around like toys placed ready for children (previous pages). Or are these excerpts from a children's book illustrated with artistic paintings?

A breccia bound with quartz (1) from the USA includes a whole collection of pieces of stone, broken or lightly polished to roundness, of the most varied sizes and colours, which have adhered together to form one stone – the result of an accident that has led to a homogeneous image. A similar impression is given by a Crazy Lace Agate (2), whose developmental history is entirely different and rather suggests culinary associations: a crabmeat terrine, a dish with various sauces, or rolls of glass in the millefiori technique. We can also see glass splinters and sugar confectionary in the material of which a Ruin Agate from Germany (3) is composed. Finally, a colourful Leopardskin Rhyolith (4) is composed of striped and rounded elements.

2 | CRAZY LACE AGATE | CHIHUAHUA, MEXICO
Strange eye-shaped formations, reminiscent of glazed ceramic objects, are closely juxtaposed to form a structure, putting in mind the palette of a painter.

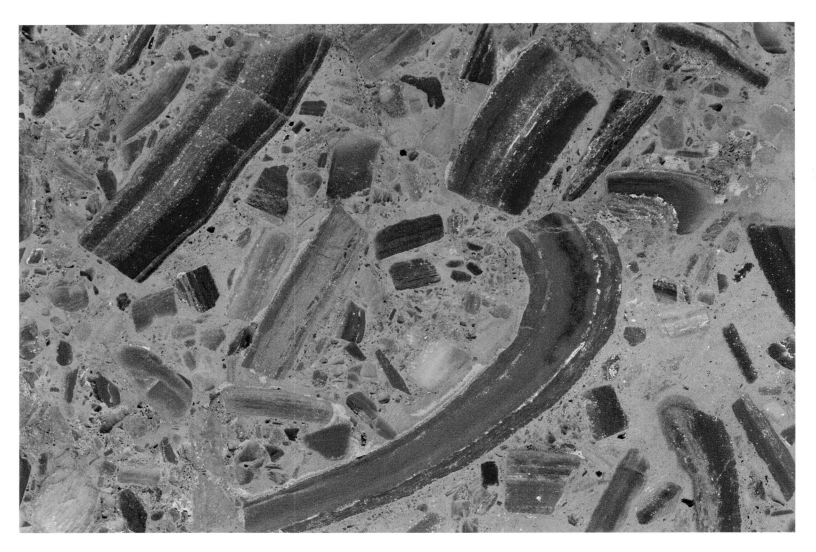

3 | **RUIN AGATE** | OBERSCHLOTTWITZ, GERMANY
Vitreous-looking fragments in a clearly defined colour spectrum
have been brought together by quartz. This has produced an
attractive, homogeneous distribution, which is still full of tension.

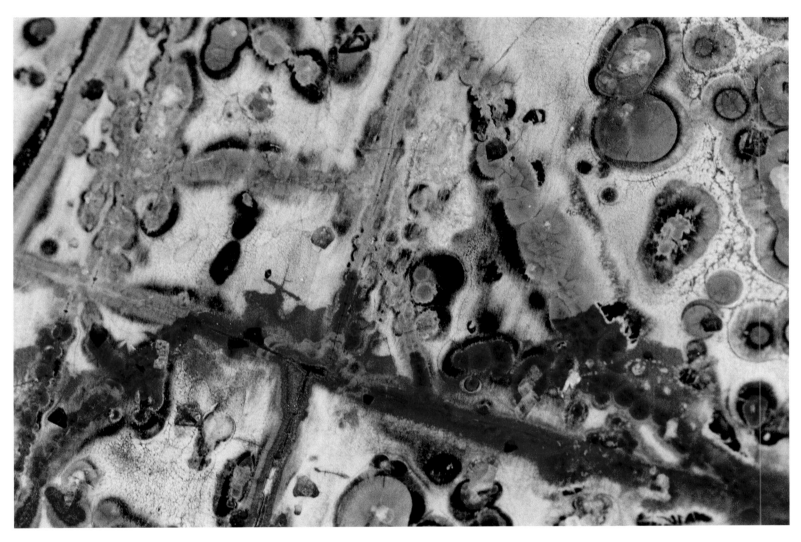

4 | **LEOPARDSKIN RHYOLITH** | MEXICO
The name of the stone already suggests a regular
distribution of patches of colour, almost a camouflage. A
stone like a picture which one can enjoy, but which refuses
to be analyzed further. The spots and lines of colour result in
a composition which may polarize opinion.

IN THE
WONDERLAND
OF ILLUSIONS

IN THE WONDERLAND OF ILLUSIONS

1 | CROSS-SECTION THROUGH A MALACHITE STALACTITE | ZAIRE, AFRICA
Stalactites are downward-growing formations caused by dripping water, which grow in layers from the inside out. The enrichment of the material with the copper compounds which provide the colour is variable, so that a gradation of different shades of green results, reminiscent of the annual rings of a tree. The eye is gripped as though by a whirlwind, and drawn into the depths.

Gripped by the eye of the malachite hurricane (1, 2), we are sucked in by the deep, dizzying chasm. We have finally arrived in Alice's Wonderland; the wavy agate (3) that seems to consist of a thousand layers, constantly appearing slightly displaced, could be the result of two mirrors hanging exactly opposite each other, in which the observer sees the same thing over and over again, in almost endless numbers, only displaced by a tiny amount. This finally results in a curve of parallel lines, which then leads out of the field of vision. This world of wonders is almost vertigo-inducing.

SWIRLING LAYERS AND PLAYFUL WAVES

Another agate (4) corresponds to quite a similar principle, but with its many lines it seems to want to move forward like a sea creature. It seems to draw its layers together, then, with an elegant movement which gives it thrust, it reverts to its original form.

The Imperial Jasper from Mexico (5, 6), with its overlapping colourful waves, shows us a play of pure colour and form, full of movement and beauty. Here we find ourselves in the Art Nouveau of geology.

2 | MALACHITE | MASHAMBA, KATANGA, ZAIRE, AFRICA
A large stalactite has swallowed up another, smaller and younger one. The lines formed later grow around the unequal pair, until it is only possible to recognize through a small bulge on the outside that there were once two stalactites here.

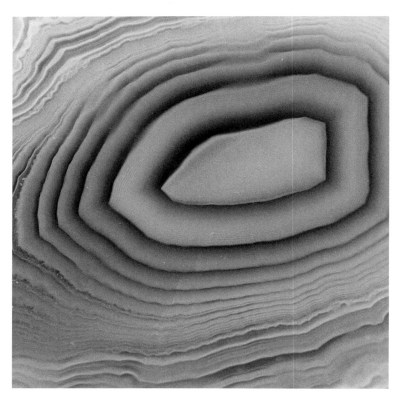

3 | **AGATE** | MASHATU, BOTSWANA, AFRICA
With these forms, placed within each other like flower petals, it is the cut that creates the work of art. The original idea in the innermost form is repeated in ever new variations.

4 | **AGATE** | MASHATU, BOTSWANA, AFRICA
The drunken agate: there is no line that does not entirely enclose the centre, but with a curving freedom which arouses enthusiasm.

5 | **IMPERIAL JASPER** | CHIHUAHUA, MEXICO
A movement resembling breaking waves in a stunningly
beautiful, limited colouring makes this jasper into a work of
art. The effect is similar to that of marble inlaid work such as
one sees in Florence. The form is also reminiscent of plant
forms, of unrolling ferns, which the artists of the Art
Nouveau period admired so much.

154

6 | **IMPERIAL JASPER** | CHIHUAHUA, MEXICO
The same stone as on the facing page, in a different colour
palette and with an even more heightened motion, suddenly
appears much more dramatic, perhaps even more menacing,
than in the sombre and mysterious colouration.

CLOUDS AND UNDERWATER IMPRESSIONS

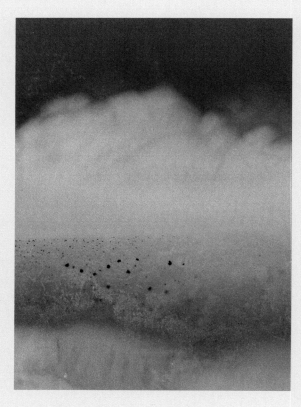

7 | AGATE | BRAZIL
Polished stones create moods. A storm is brewing: flat cloud cover seems to be towered over by high cumulus clouds.

Opposite:
8 | AGATE | OREGON, USA
Although a sky of bright clouds lies above it, the valley seems to be a valley of sorrow. The mood is like that of a Wagner opera. On looking closely, one can discern once again the familiar elements of the agate's form, the curves and straight lines.

Agates (7–10), which, like changing climatic conditions, evoke menacing, reassuring or even hallucinatory moods, lead us into further imaginary spaces and moods. If you choose to see a landscape in it, with clouds above reddish-yellow desert expanses, you will be enthusiastic about this mirage. But one can also see meditative images in it. One would like to see it in large format, two metres wide, at least the size of a Mark Rothko painting.

The agates from India have a similar magic, except that here a sombre sky full of streaks of cloud appears to extend indefinitely (11). Is this a Moorish citadel that appears here in the last ray of sunlight before a threatening storm, before the hurricane breaks loose (12)? Rigid inclusions in the regular layering of a Pink Jasper evoke an underworld full of vegetable remains or the long feelers of various types of crustaceans (13, 14). Similar horizontal structures are invaded by thread- and mycelia-like formations (15–18). They crowd into the image like long lichens hanging from trees, in which one can become hopelessly caught up. We see such threatening creepers in cartoon films, reminding us from afar of the surrealistic creations of H.R. Giger. But with a little more calm, we can also see structures of contemporary craftworks: pieces of jewellery, gold-encrusted glass or luxurious fabrics, interspersed with lace and brocade. The Indian heliotrope too (19–21) seems to show an underwater world, with many spongy formations and plankton. The red spots create a hologram effect on the green background, and if one fixes one's gaze on these red spots, it seems to dive into the depths. With the reddish-green fluorite (22, 23) however, the water is frozen, and the eye is drawn deep into its shining fracture points. A red mouth, frozen fluids – all these interpretations are possible!

9 | **AGATE** | BRAZIL
Here one can only admire the stunning beauty of the layers
of stone, the white bands separated by red or ochre-coloured
lines, in which, phase by phase, areas of macrocrystalline
quartz shine out. But one can also feel uplifted here, high
above the clouds.

10 | **AGATE** | MASHATU, BOTSWANA, AFRICA
While with many agates it is the stupendous clarity and
precision of the lines that fascinate us, here it is the diffuse,
the cloudy, that has us under its spell. The variety shown by
these polished stones is overpowering.

11 | **AGATE** | DECCAN PLATEAU, BOMBAY, INDIA
The irregularity in the regular makes this stone into a work
of art. One cannot be blind to the mood transmitted by
these incredibly harmonious shades of grey and beige, rich
in variations.

12 | **AGATE** | DECCAN PLATEAU, BOMBAY, INDIA
Sombre colours can also be very beautiful when they are so
finely attuned to each other. In a rather dark atmosphere, a
ray of sunlight penetrating the banks of cloud seems to light
up an object and pick it out like a searchlight.

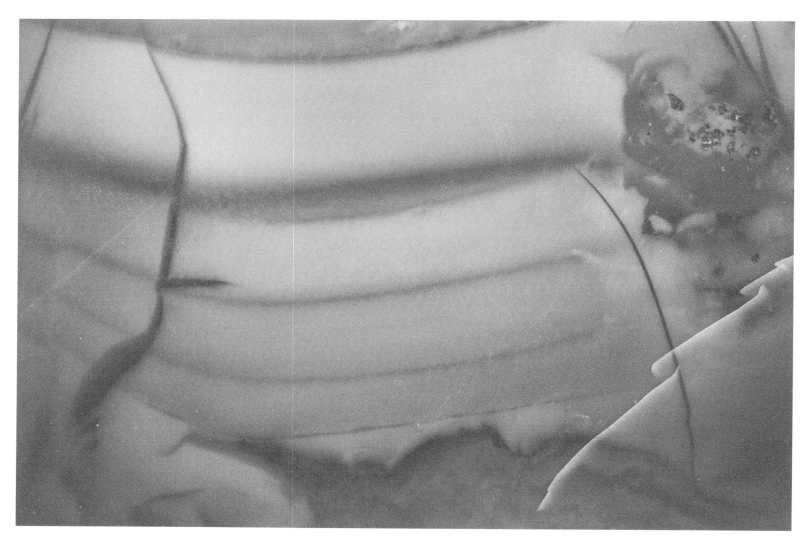

13 | **PINK JASPER** | MEXICO
Coral red and shell-pink are combined in this jasper, which
with its colour and because of the red lines that seem to
represent the sensory organs of crabs, reminds us of
crustaceans and allows a mood to emerge that is familiar to
us from underwater images.

160

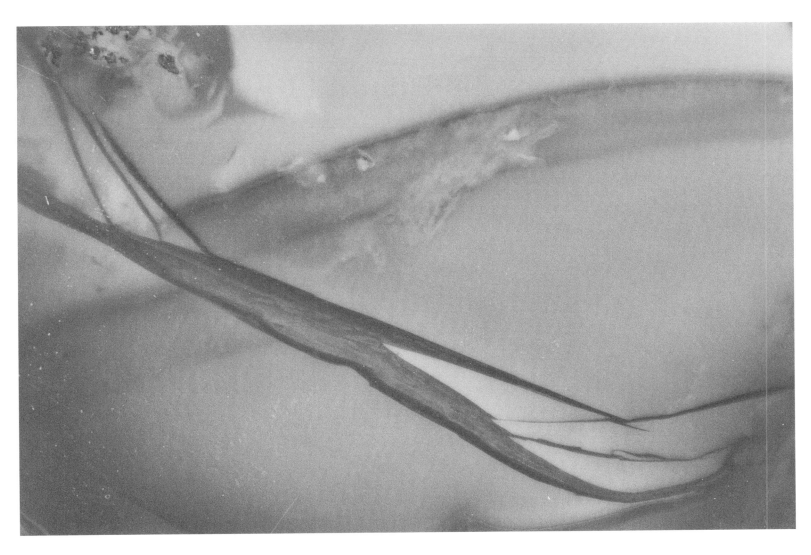

14 | **PINK JASPER** | MEXICO
In the quiet, gentle transitions of colour in this milky-rosy
jasper the hard red lines have the effect of the lash of a
whip.

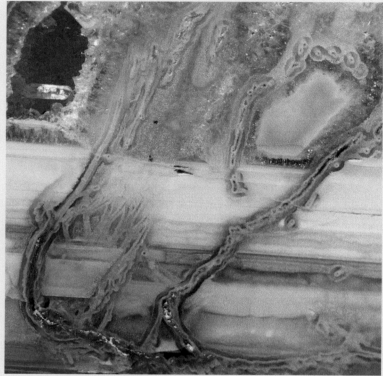

15 | **MOSS AGATE** | BRITISH COLUMBIA, CANADA
Against a light background we see again the familiar parallel
lines of the agate. The lichen-like formations intrude into
this stone like foreign bodies, but it is precisely the contrast
between the quiet 'background' and the alien, sombre,
embedded particles, like decomposing organic substances,
that gives this image its tension.

16 | **MOSS AGATE** | BRITISH COLUMBIA, CANADA
The organic-seeming, rootlike formations look like they have
gained access to this substratum and are living off it. At the
top right of the photograph, distorted parts of a closed chain
seem to have been left behind. But the magic of the image
also goes back to the opening, shining like a crystal cavern,
above left, which seems to enclose a mysterious rock crystal.

162

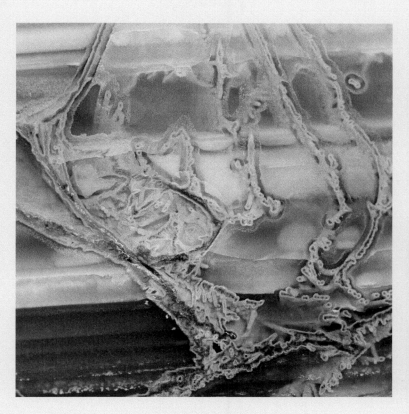

17 | **MOSS AGATE** | BRITISH COLUMBIA, CANADA
Like a golden ornament, the incrustations here seem to lie on
top of the agate. Since these formations, which look like
roots, are themselves hollows which have grown together
again, they too were opened when the stone was cut. Where
they are vertical in relation to the cut, they are visible as rings.

18 | **PINK JASPER** | MEXICO
In contrast to the order that reigns, more or less, in the
agates, this jasper is a tangle of lines. But here too we can
make out the centre of disturbance in the centre of the
image. The eye focuses on it, only to wander into the
peripheral area to see where repercussions are evident, for
example the displacement at the top right of the image.

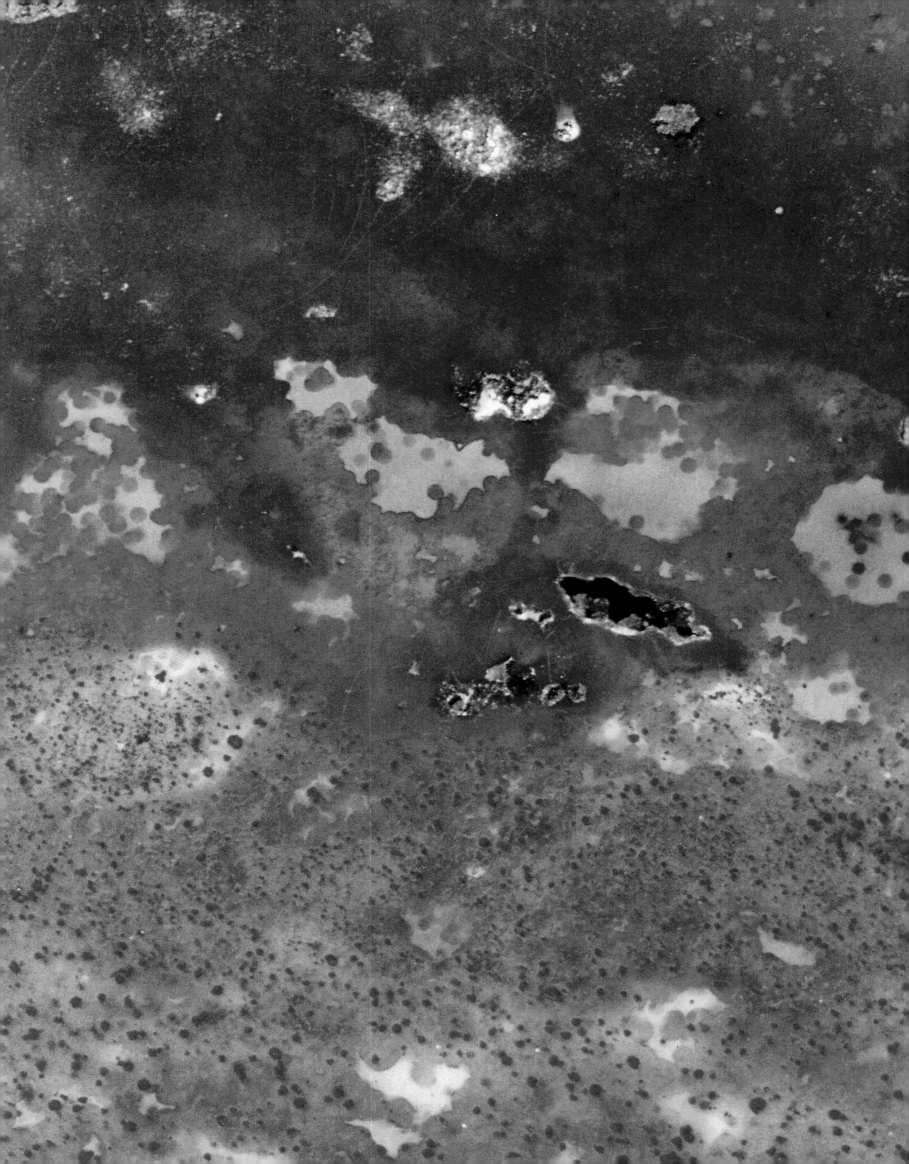

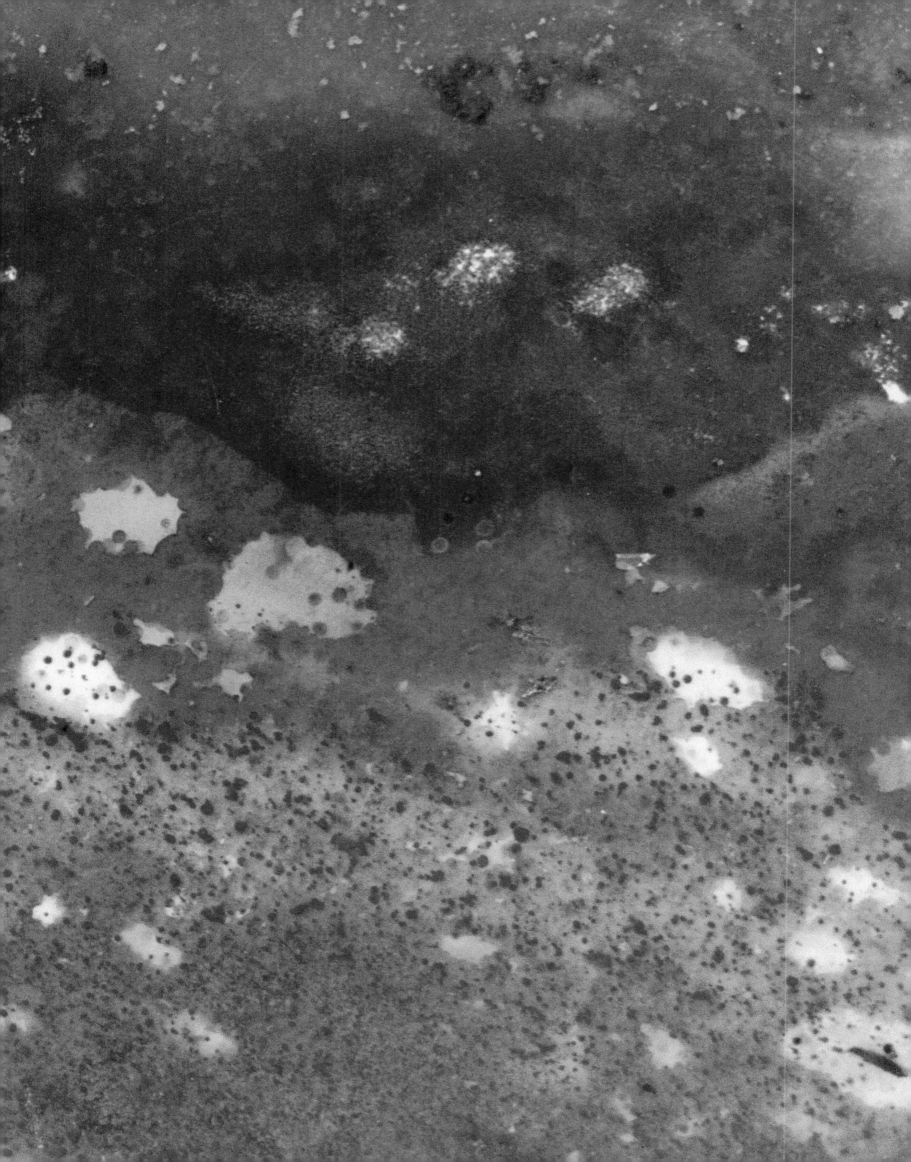

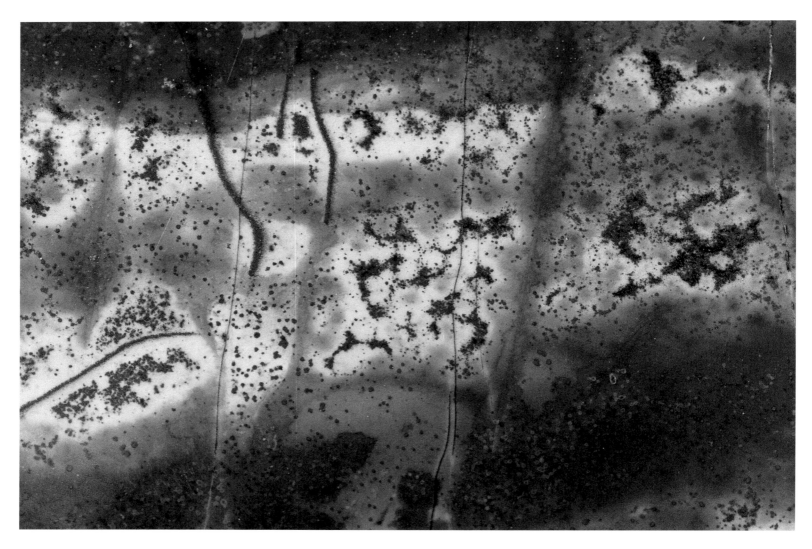

20 | BLOODSTONE (HELIOTROPE) | INDIA
The chequered surface with the hairline fractures of the
upper surface reminds one of Asian ceramics. Perhaps it was
so worn away by touch over the centuries that the white
basic layer, even the brown colour in these areas, is
prominent. But the polished surface of this heliotrope is
interesting even without any associations.

Previous pages:
19 | BLOODSTONE (HELIOTROPE) | INDIA
A deep-sea landscape, painted in pointillist or impressionist
style? If one fixes the eye on one of the red dots in the
foreground, the depths seem to open up as in a hologram.

21 | BLOODSTONE (HELIOTROPE) | INDIA
This stone too, gives the impression of a hologram. The
varying frequency of the red dots creates a sort of magnet
for the eye; one would like to gaze for ever into these
mysterious depths.

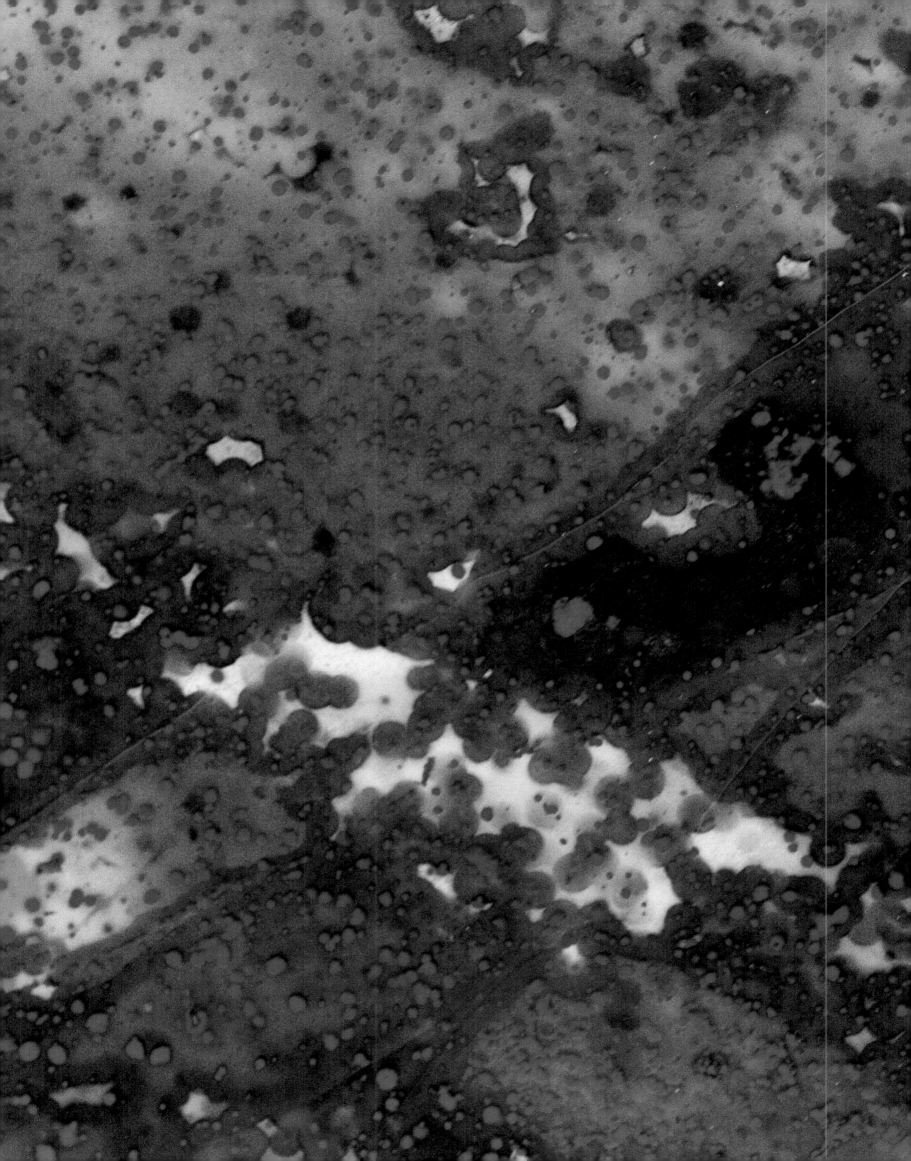

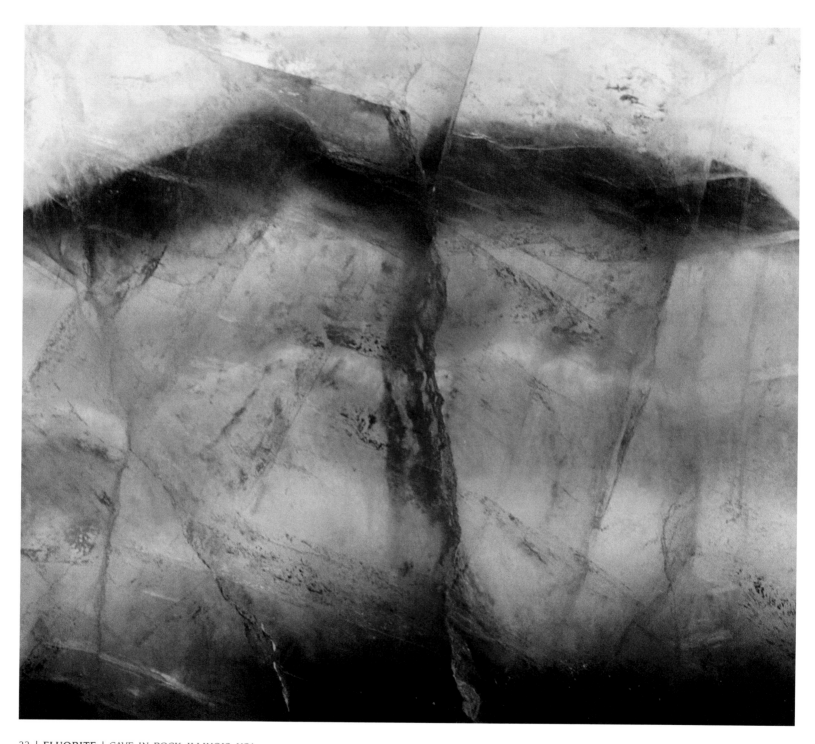

22 | FLUORITE | CAVE-IN-ROCK, ILLINOIS, USA
Even more alluring is the attraction to the eye of this fluorite
crystal, which is highly transparent and seems to tease the
observer with its delicate colorations of bottle-green, grass-
green and amethyst purple. The colouring here is basically
geometric, running along the potential fracture lines of
the crystal.

23 | **FLUORITE** | CAVE-IN-ROCK, ILLINOIS, USA
Most of the stones in this book are microcrystalline
formations, with the exception of the Rutile Quartz on page
32 and these two fluorites. The fluorite may crystallize in an
octahedral or cubic form.

SATELLITE
IMAGES

SATELLITE IMAGES

1 | **AGATE** | RIO GRANDE DO SUL, BRAZIL
An agate with its typical forms, but also a coastal landscape with sandbanks, constantly gnawed at by the ebbing tide, and marshes.

Opposite:
2 | **AGATE, THUNDER EGG** | OREGON, USA
A coastal landscape with islands and shallows, bays and rocky promontories, even houses or trees, streams or roads.

As has already been mentioned in the introduction, very close observation of our world produces results which remind us strikingly of the view from a long distance. Satellite images or aerial photographs that show coastlines or meandering rivers, which carry their cargo of sediments with them far into the sea, where the colour of the fresh water slowly mingles with the colour of the sea, are strikingly similar to certain agates: promontories, fjords, bays and islands can be made out, which are considerably longer than the abbreviated lines on the map, and lagoons and sandbars can also be found.

COASTLINES AND ISLANDS

Sometimes one seems (1–3) to be looking at aerial shots taken from a great height. The sea is shallow, one has a sense of the sea bed, islands are bounded by sandy beaches, and on the gently yellow-green land there seem to be signs of agriculture to be made out, interrupted here and there by traffic routes. Bushes or small forests accentuate the coastal region. An agate showing a sculpturally projecting hill (3), reminds one of a school atlas. We interpret the bands of the agate as altitude curves and are surprised that the corresponding hill is still shaded, as it would be on the map. Waves could be water or sand dunes (4). Promontories branching out with broad shorelines, where the water-level can be read from the ebb and flow (5, 6), show quite similar variations of colour, as we see from satellite images; the colours change according to the position on the globe, and the fertility of the land.

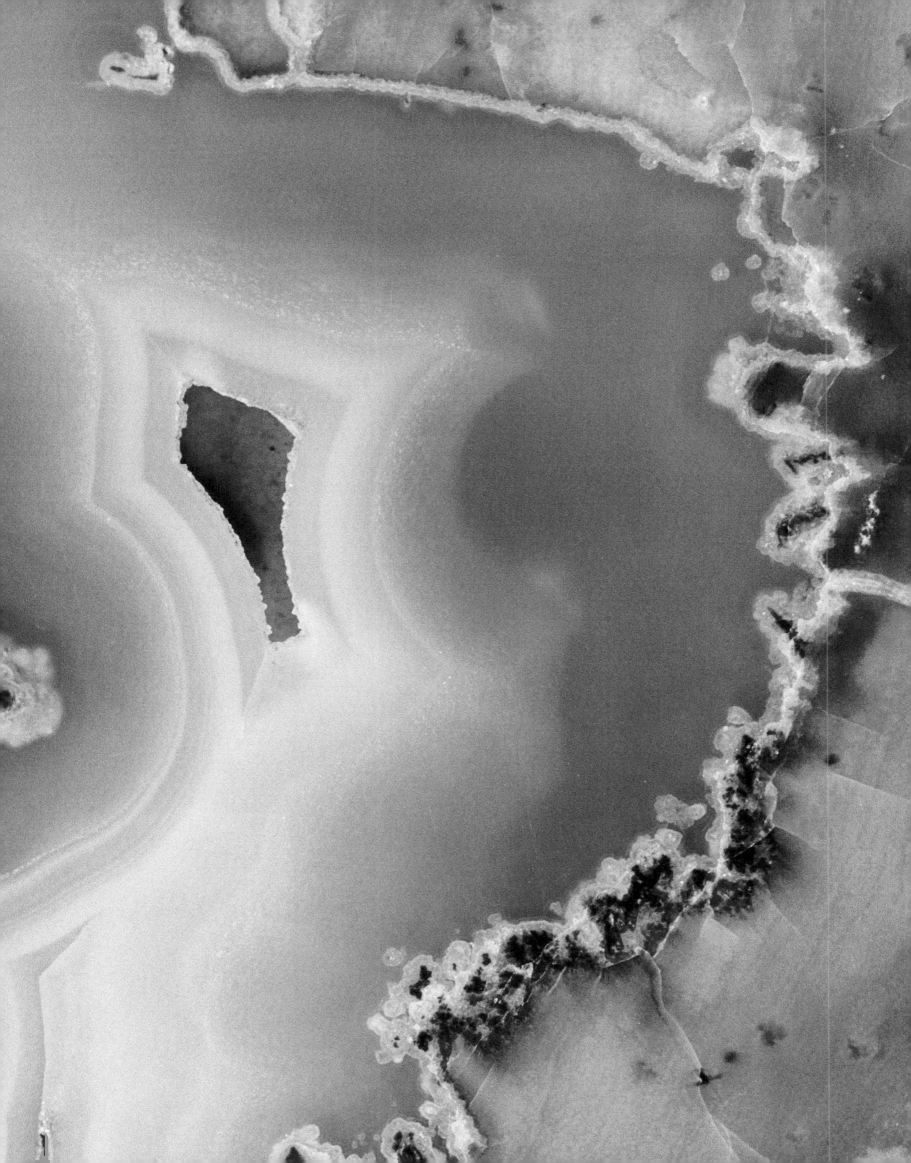

3 | **AGATE** | CHIHUAHUA, MEXICO
Yet another of these magnificent agates with a theme and
variations. On the other side of a hill – with its altitude
curves as seen on old maps – is a precise casting of shadow,
which only emphasizes the sculptural quality.

4 | **AGATE** | HIGH ATLAS, MOROCCO
Agate lines, in one case running nicely parallel and more or
less straight, in another (right) rippling like the sea tide. Is it
a seashore with dunes and a settlement?

174

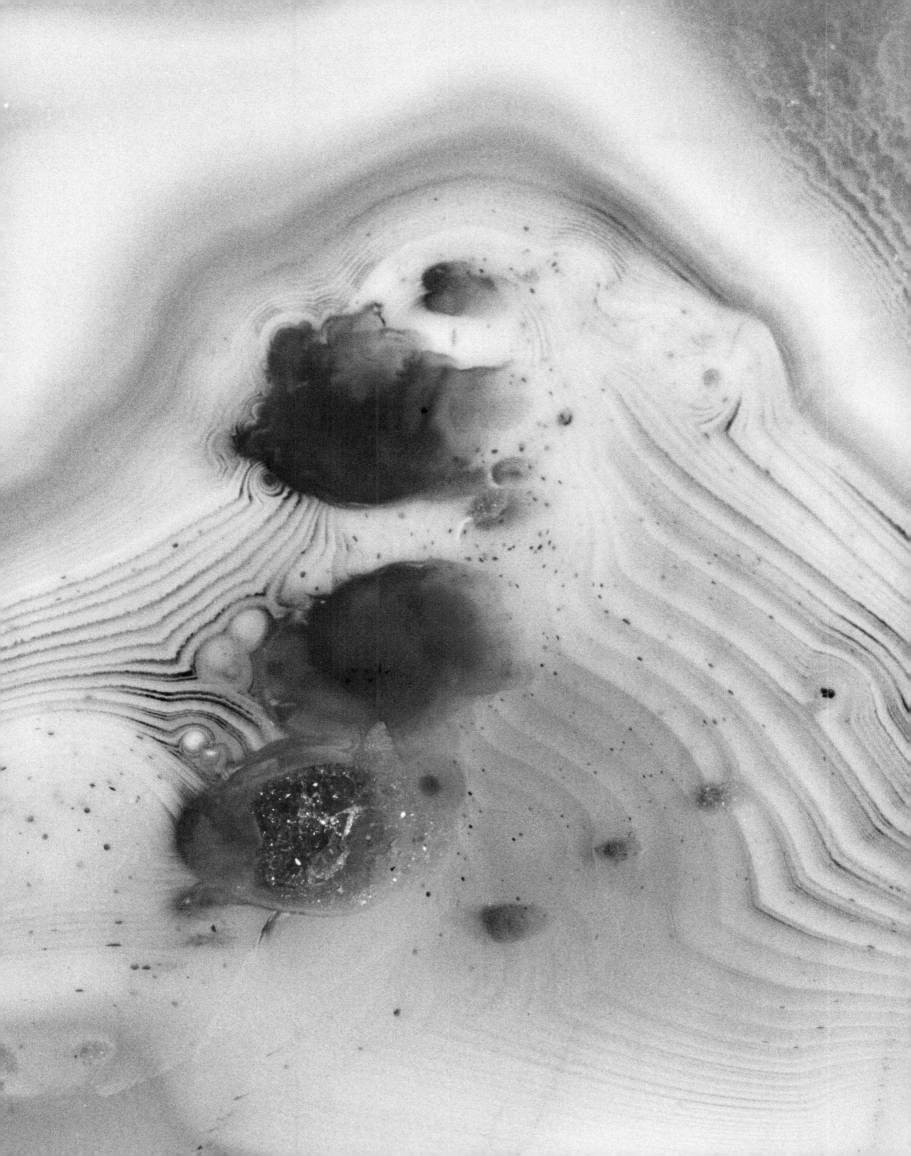

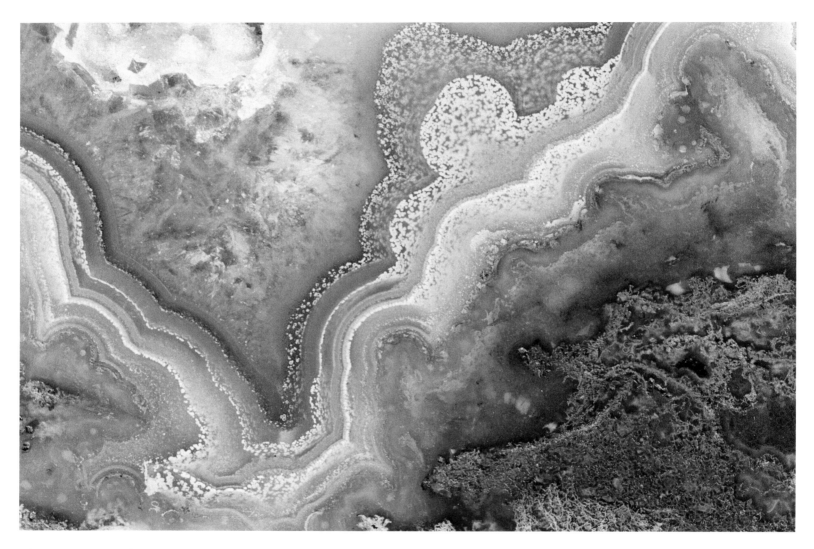

5 | **APAREJO AGATE** | CHIHUAHUA, MEXICO
A particularly beautiful agate with its almost opaline colour
tones, but also a beautiful landscape, where earth and water
meet, with shorelines, marshes and swampy forests.

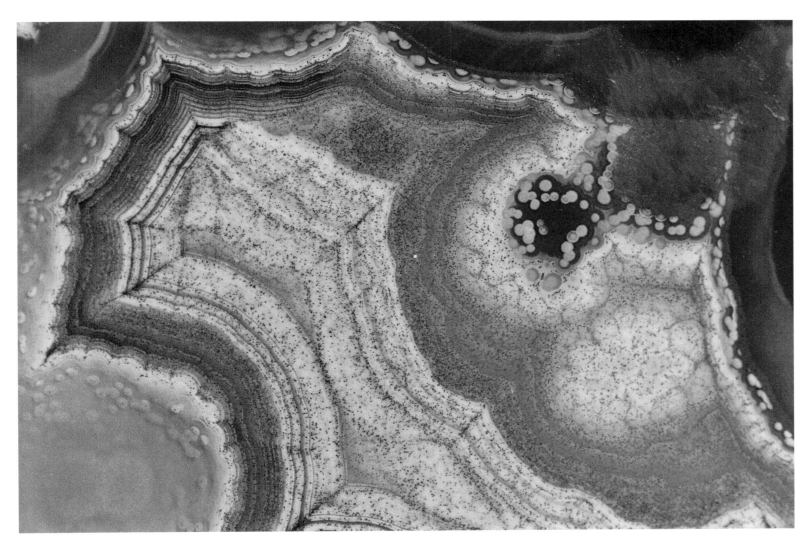

6 | **LAGUNA AGATE** | CHIHUAHUA, MEXICO
An excerpt from a map, at the rocky seashore with steep
cliffs and a low-lying harbour area.

MEANDERING RIVERS AND CANYONS

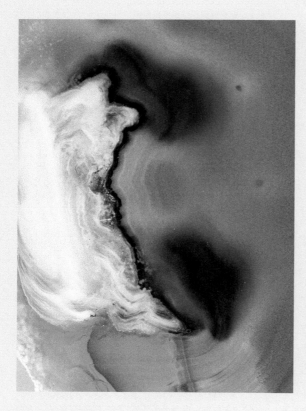

Islands and coastlines are the most interesting areas, not only in the atlases, but also in our agates (7–10). But the eroded, deeply furrowed mountain ranges are also of interest (11) with their multiple branches. Are the reddish-orange parts the dried-up valleys and the white parts the snow-covered mountains, or are the orange parts the mountainsides eroded by rivulets, streams and rivers, and the white the sandy plain of a distant desert? Perhaps even on another planet – which today's space probes allow us excellent images of? Then again, we think we can see meandering rivers, swamp landscapes such as can be seen from the air in northern Canada (12), partly surrounded by the green of luxuriant vegetation. An agate from Sicily, finally, shows us dried-out canyons (13) or the cracked clay bed of a dried-out pond. Or, here too, have frozen water deposits from another planet been discovered?

7 | **AGATE** | RIO GRANDE DO SUL, BRAZIL
Land, sea and clouds, currents in all elements

8 | **LAGUNA AGATE** | CHIHUAHUA, MEXICO
An image of unusual magic, an agate in a splendid, even if unfamiliar combination of colours, a structure with dots that slowly dive into the blurred, semi-transparent material. We can see a landscape here as well, if we like.

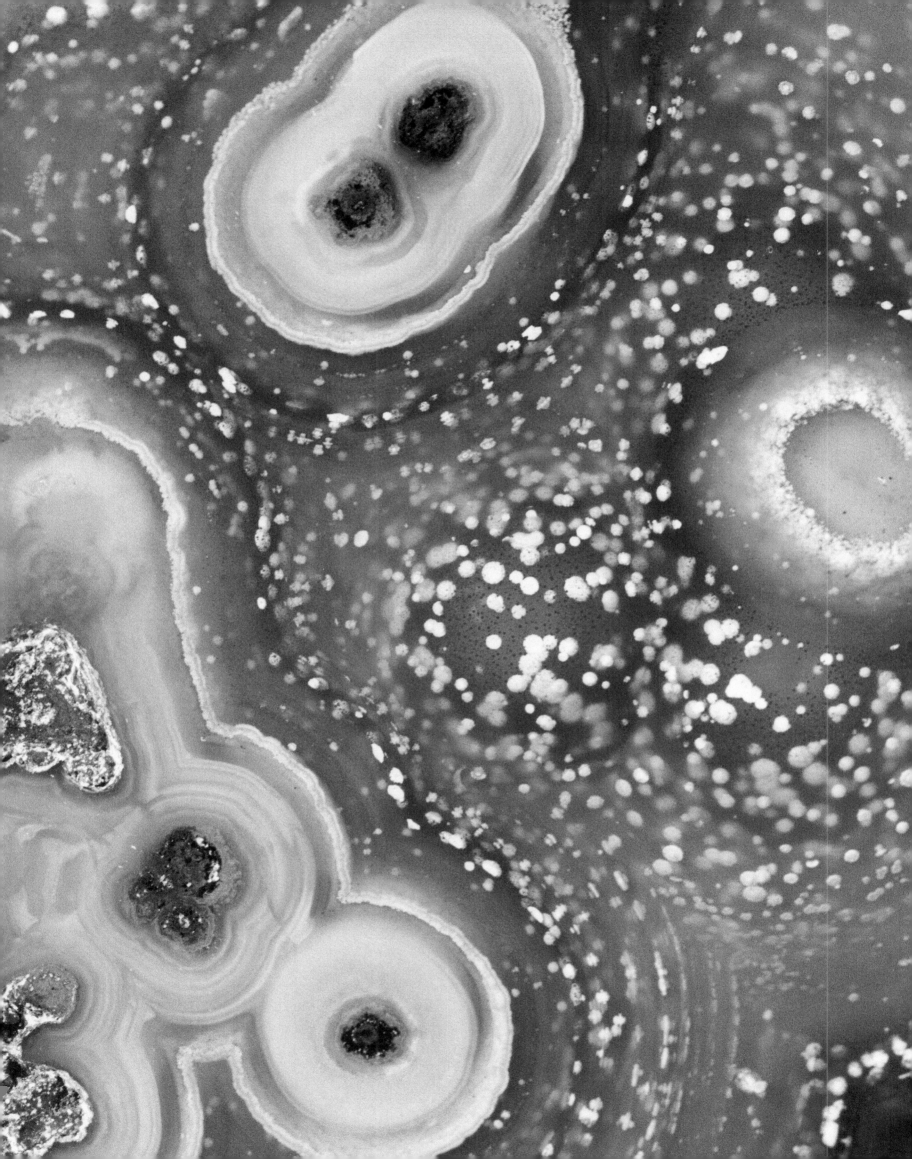

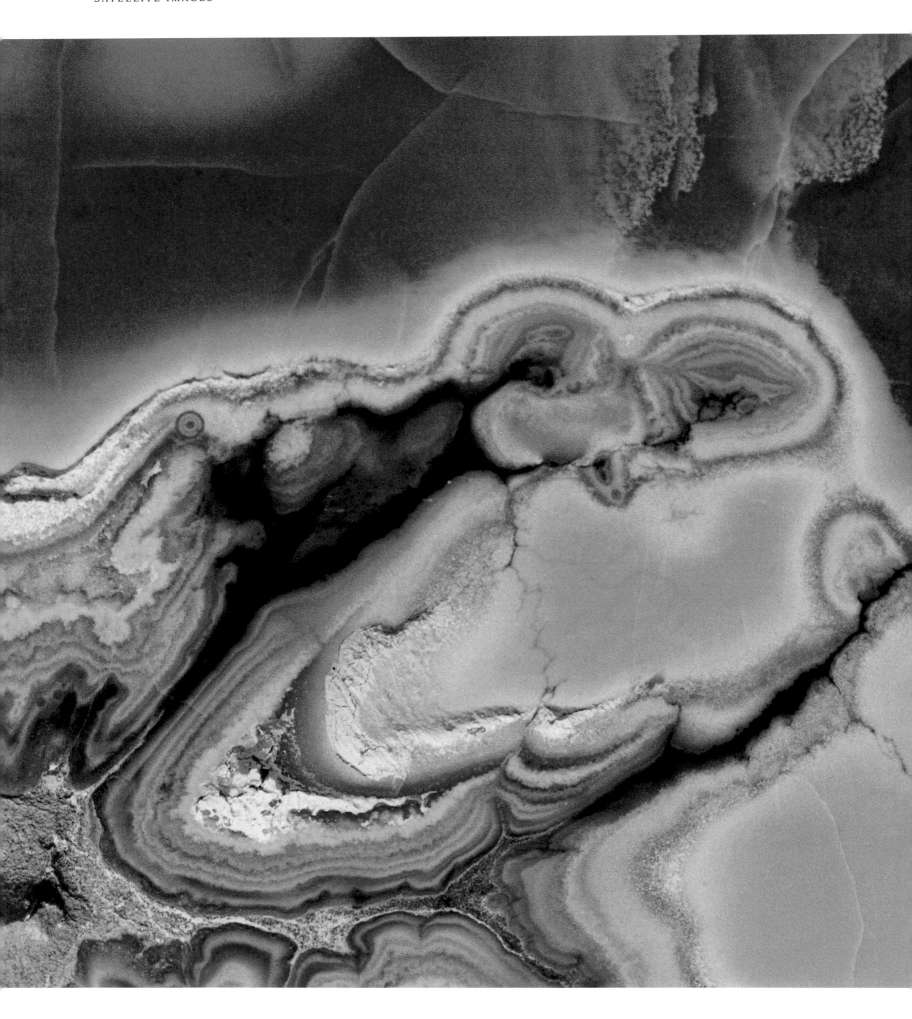

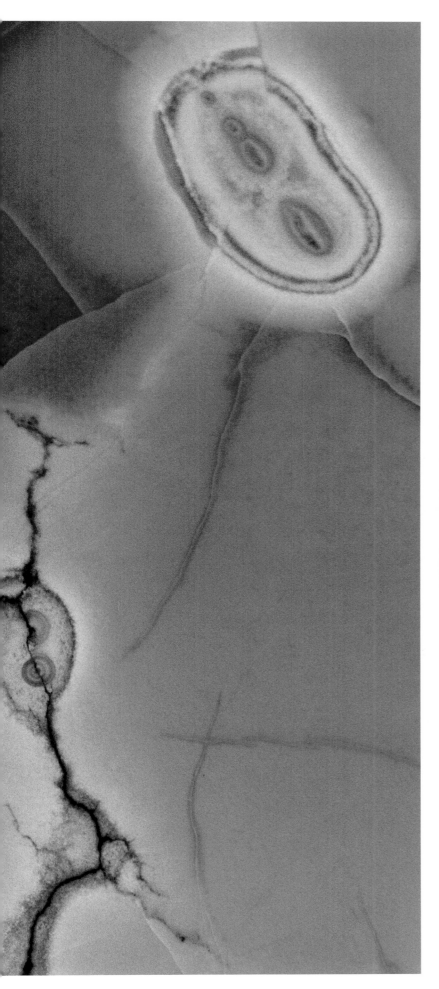

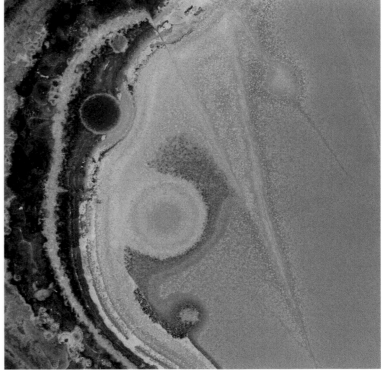

10 | **VARISCITE** | FAIRFIELD, UTAH, USA
It does not always have to be agates that evoke the impression
of landscape images. This variscite could show a bay enclosed
by a sandy beach and a wooded hilly area.   -

Left: 9 | **VARISCITE** | FAIRFIELD, UTAH, USA
A variscite in a strong green, in which we may see the
ravening throat of a monster or a landscape shot taken from
a great height. Everything is left to the imagination and to
personal associations. A Venetian carnival mask beside the
face of an alien?

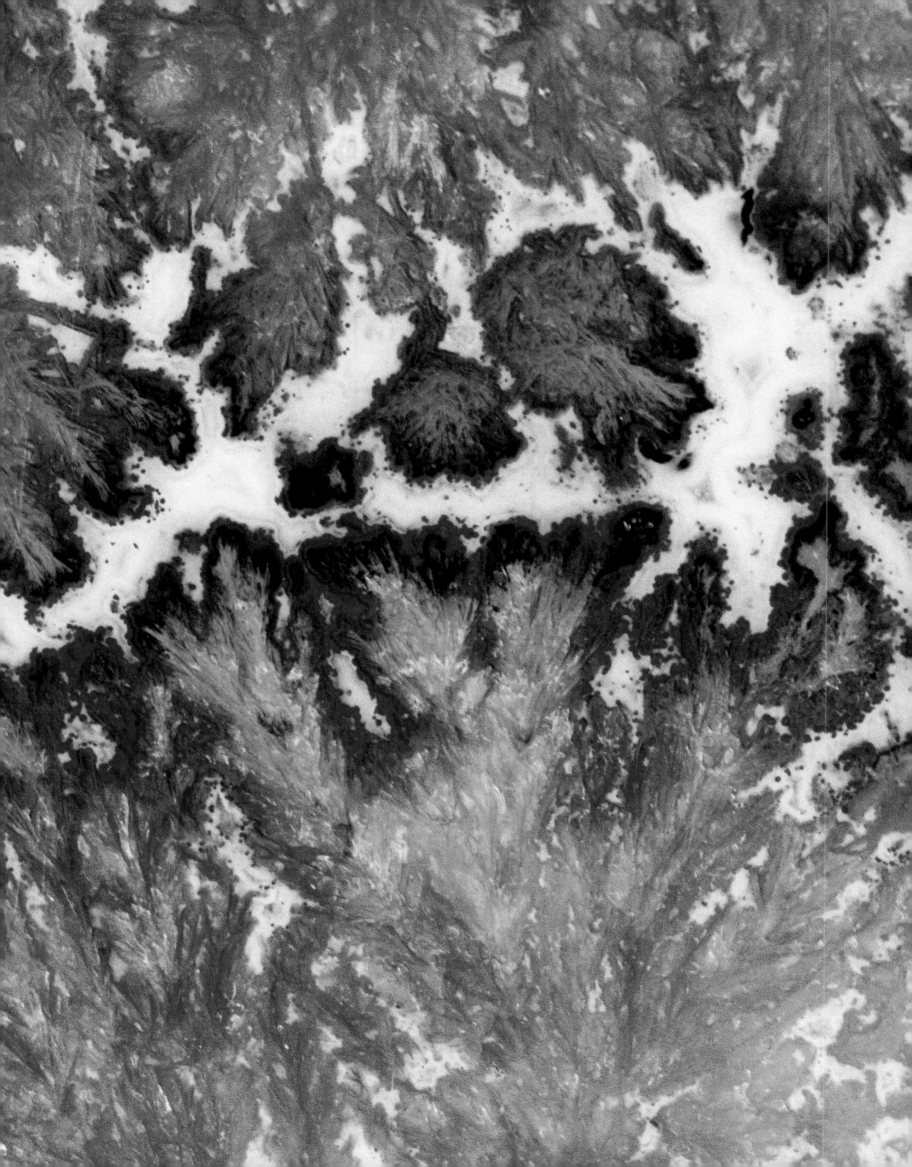

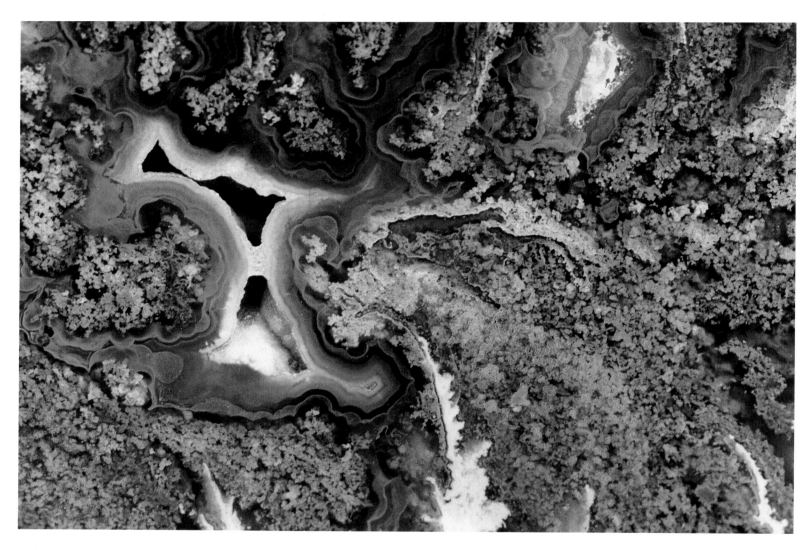

12 | **AGATE** | GRAVEYARD POINT, OREGON, USA
Autumnal woods with partially frozen lakes and banks of fog
over the mountains. Or quite simply a totally wild agate.

Previous pages:
11 | **PLUME AGATE** | OREGON, USA
From a distance we seem to see a snow-covered mountain
landscape with valleys washed out by erosion, while from a
closer point of view these are rather reddish-yellow snow-
less mountain ranges, which flow into white-based valleys.

13 | **AGATE** | SICILY, ITALY
Dried-out desert landscape with deeply notched valleys – or
the cracked clay bed of a dried-out lake. Perhaps an image of
Mars, such as no space probe sent out so far has been able to
transmit to us, with a little frozen water.

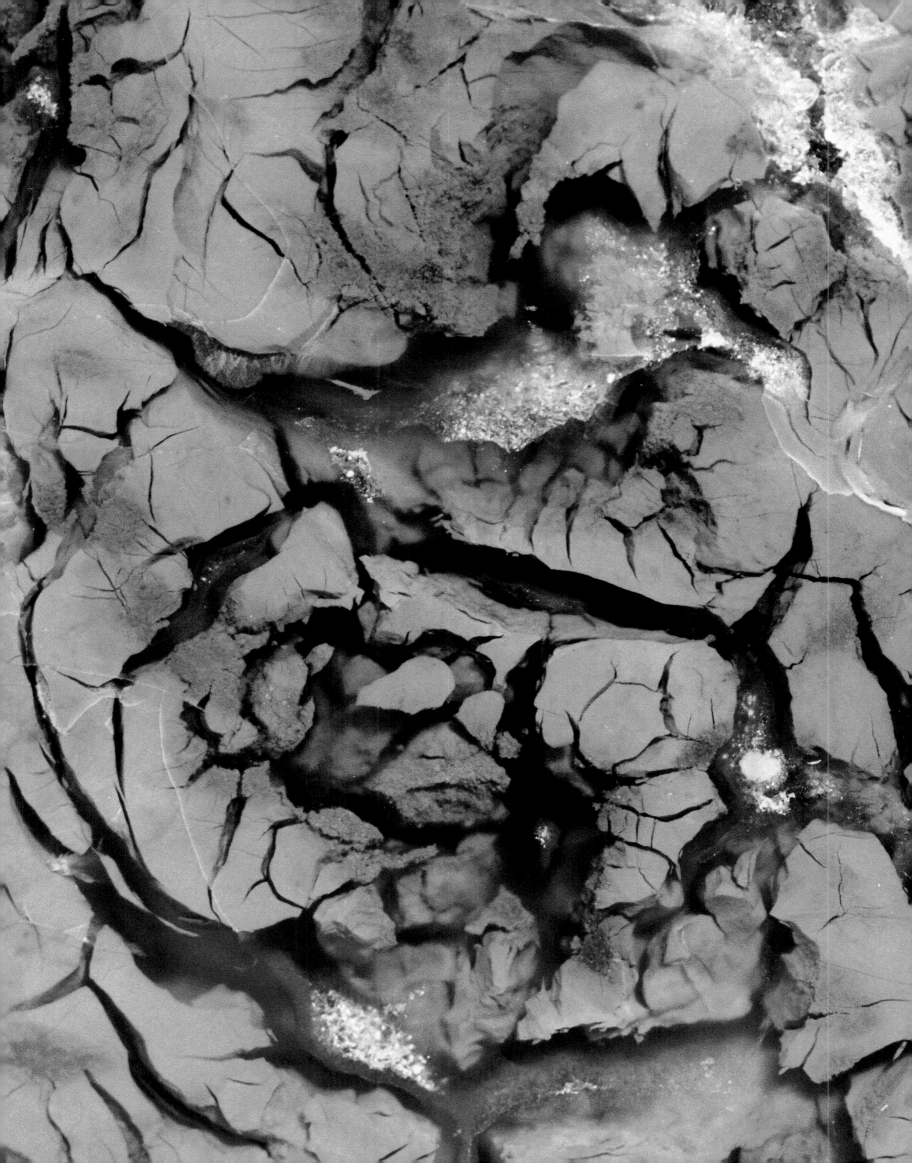

CONCRETE
AND
ABSTRACT

CONCRETE AND ABSTRACT

1 | **LAYER AGATE** | CHIHUAHUA, MEXICO
Art? A technological structure? A somewhat confused street
network in a disorientated agglomeration?

But let us again approach the concrete or abstract.
Contemporary art has developed hardly anything that did
not already exist in nature, in stones – only perhaps the eye
had to be trained by becoming used to the art in order to
discover it in the stone. That exact geometric forms appear
in the macrocrystalline world is the logical consequence of
their chemical composition. The cubes of pyrites or of sodium
chloride, the spheres of marcasite, the octahedrons of fluorite
are well known. But that related geometric figures occur in
materials that have been cut can probably be explained
above all by the effect of pressure in combination with the
folds of mountains.

SURFACES OF CONCRETE ART

The Layer Agate from Mexico (1) formed a lattice structure
that then became filled with a crystalline mass, which now
looks like an aerial shot of an urban street network – not to
put too much of a strain on the art of the 20th century. An
almost three-dimensional impression is given by the
structures of the cut iron nickel meteorites (previous pages
and 2). Here, physics has created an amalgamation of
concrete art. The fracture lines of the stone plates from the
Val d'Arno (3, 4) remind us of paintings by the artist Lyonel
Feininger, but in their playful regularity of changing colours
they also anticipate many elements of concrete painting.

2 | **IRON NICKEL METEORITE** | GIBEON METEORITE
FALL, GREAT NAMA LAND, NAMIBIA, AFRICA
The so-called Widmannstatten patterns form a delightful
play of geometric forms, but if one 'reads' the photograph
three-dimensionally, one sees a building site with many iron
girders – the construction of the façades and ceilings is still
to come.

3 | **VERDE D'ARNO** | FLORENCE, ITALY
Almost as with the concrete artists, every cut surface
appears in a different shade of colour.

4 | **VERDE D'ARNO** | FLORENCE, ITALY
Many fractured surfaces result in many triangles and these
again are repeatedly found in different colours. Almost as
when one lays polarized discs turned at a 90-degree angle
on top of each other; the colour becomes darker and darker,
because less and less light can penetrate.

ENTWINED CELTIC BANDS

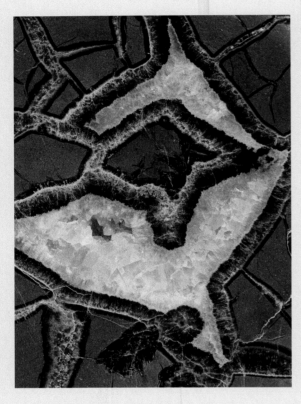

5 | **SEPTARIUM (CALCITE)** | KANE CO., UTAH, USA
Wild ornamentation, partly filled in with calcite crystals.

Opposite:
6 | **SEPTARIUM (CALCITE)** | SAN SEBASTIAN, SPAIN
A pattern with repeated slightly displaced connections. The
pattern suggests Celtic ornamentation. The Pre-Raphaelite
artist Edward Burne-Jones painted Sidonia von Bork in a
dress with a similar band pattern.

The calcite septaria (5–7) create forms reminiscent of the
ornamentation of Celtic art. The ornaments turn into wild
dragon patterns or pretzel-shaped formations. Another
pretty pattern is that of the argyllite from Australia (8),
described not without reason as zebra stone. Like a confused
network or a fine weaving, set with shining stones, a pyrite
stone from the USA presents itself (9). As to the dendrites
(little trees) on Solnhofen plates and Eaglewood Limestone
(10–12) from South Dakota, it should be recorded that these
are fine crystal formations, which developed into minute
hollows when the corresponding rock began to split into
plates under the pressure of the formation of folds. The
dendrites on agate (13, 14) make us think of a delightful
evening pool landscape: diffused, dreamy, romantic. The lobe
lines with their very similar effect (15, 16), which come from
ammonites (a kind of petrified nautilus), are on the other
hand totally organic, but of zoological, not vegetable origin.
The nautilus (17), 170 million years old, and the ammonite (18),
'only' 20 million years younger, from Madagascar, show in the
most beautiful way the regular structure of the spiral of the
shell, filled with crystalline material in various colours.

Chaos and order, the uncertain, the vague and the concrete
are shown to us by these cut stones. The Greek word 'cosmos'
refers to both ornament and order, including the whole world
order. If we believe we have found some principles of order in
the images in this book, we should not forget first of all to
enjoy the ornament, the beauty, of which they give us such a
deep impression.

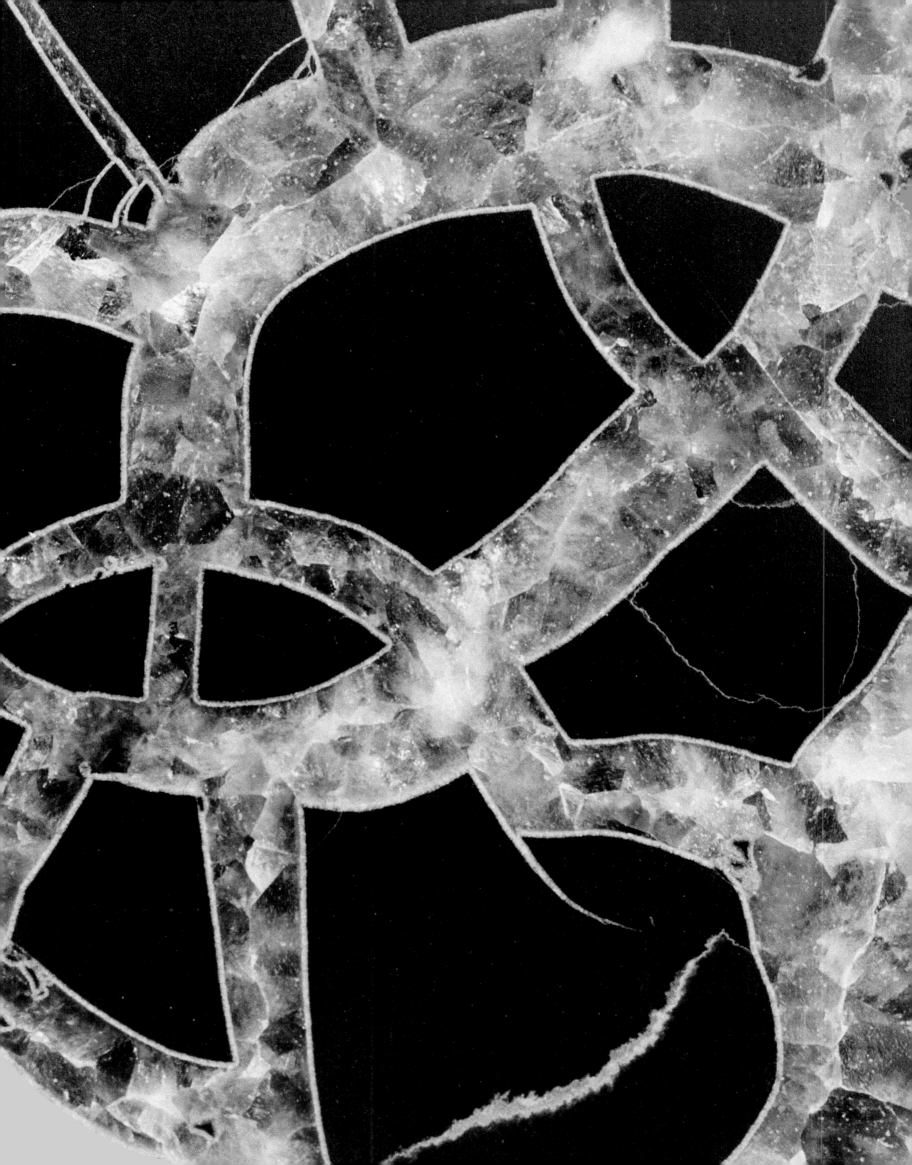

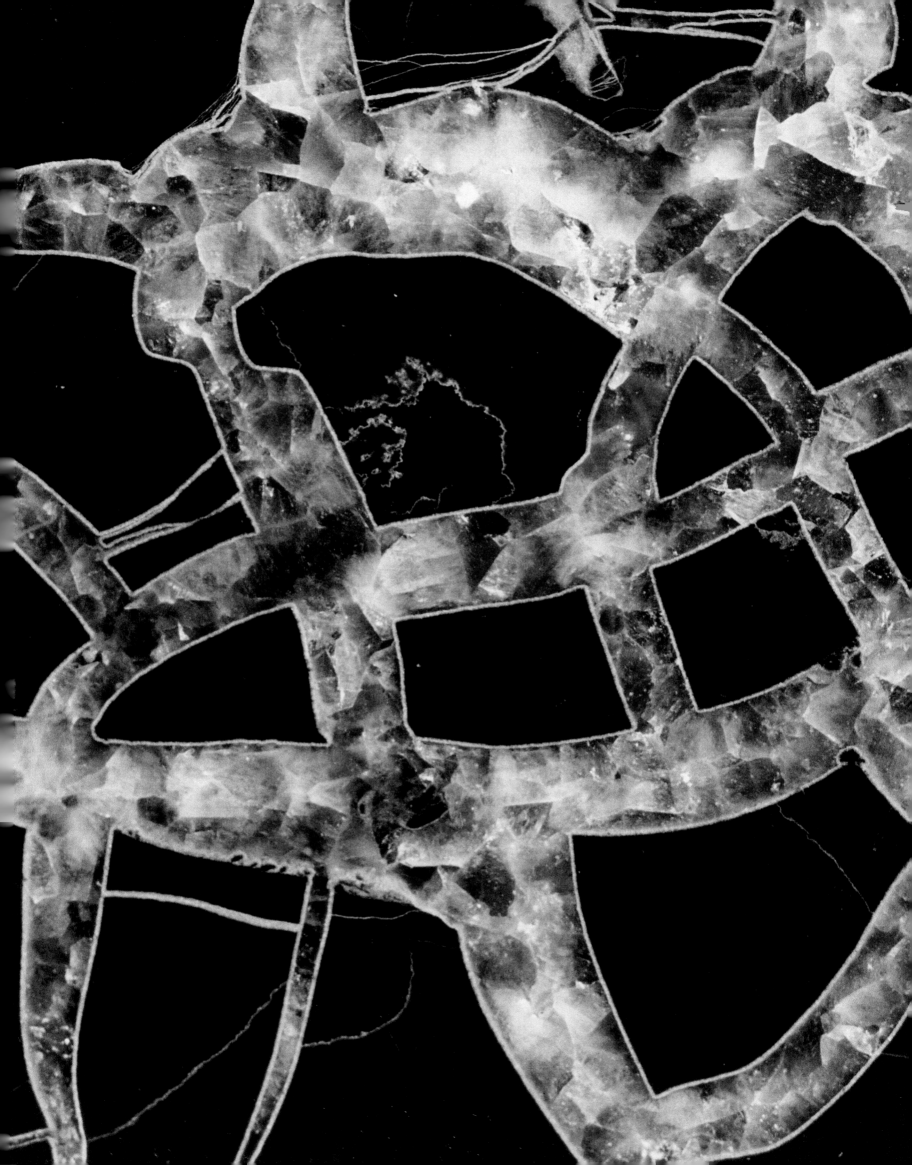

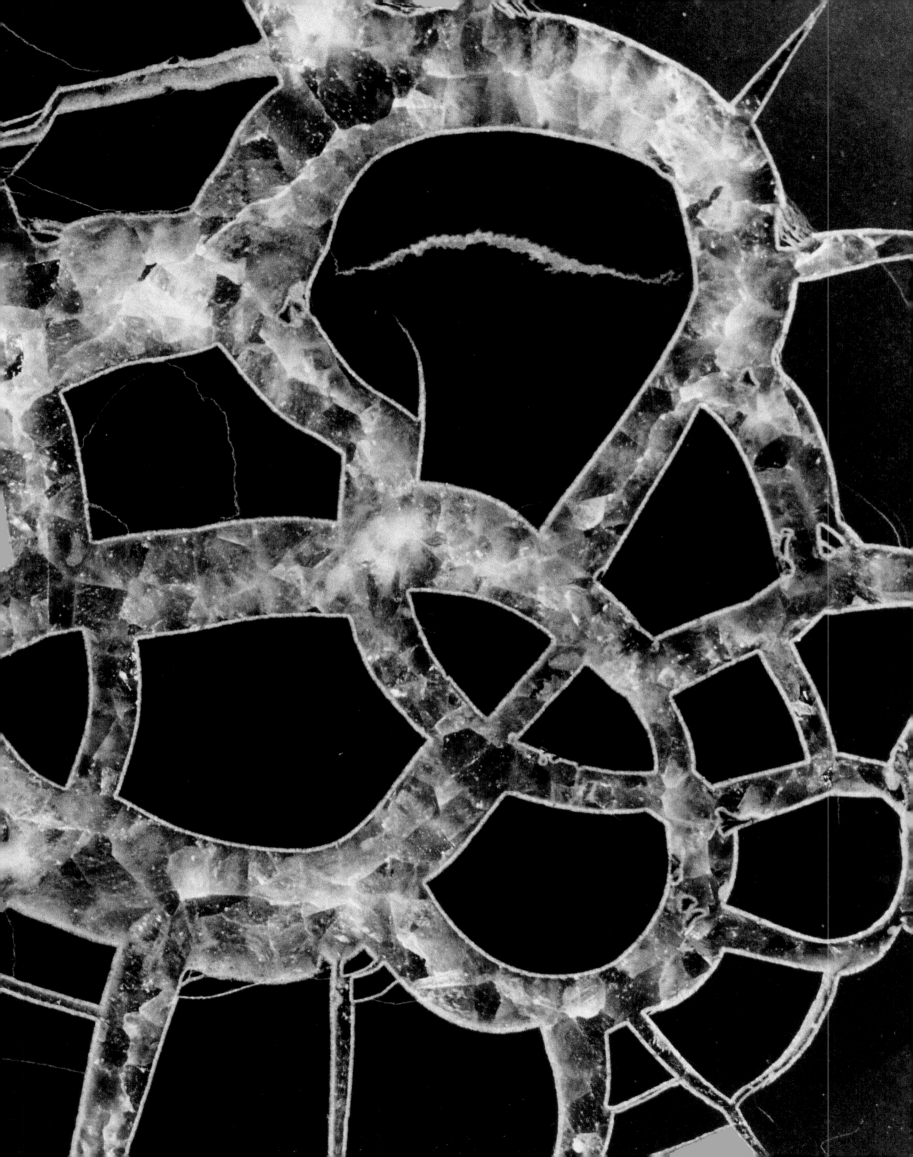

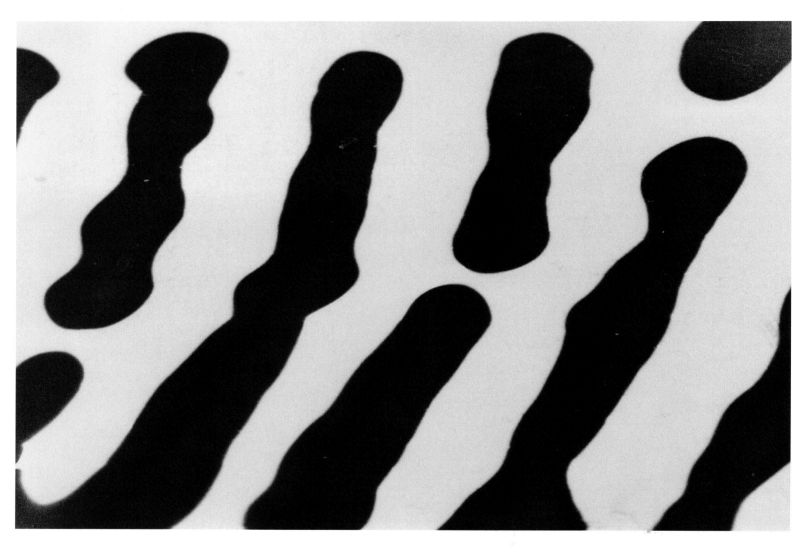

8 | **ARGILLITE (ZEBRA STONE)** | KANUMURRA,
WESTERN AUSTRALIA
A perfect pattern with a regular rhythm.

Previous pages:
7 | **SEPTARIUM (CALCITE)** | SAN SEBASTIAN, SPAIN
A pattern resembling wickerwork. Everything seems to be
connected to everything else.

9 | **PYRITE AGATE** | USA
A net-like, milling confusion, which – although of course not
textile – looks very much like a woven article, but on the
other hand is also reminiscent of the net in which a butcher
wraps meat to be roasted. The impression of knotted metal
wires in a kind of brocade is strengthened by the
shimmering dots of colour, whose sheen reminds us of
pearls – a modern textile with gems woven into it?

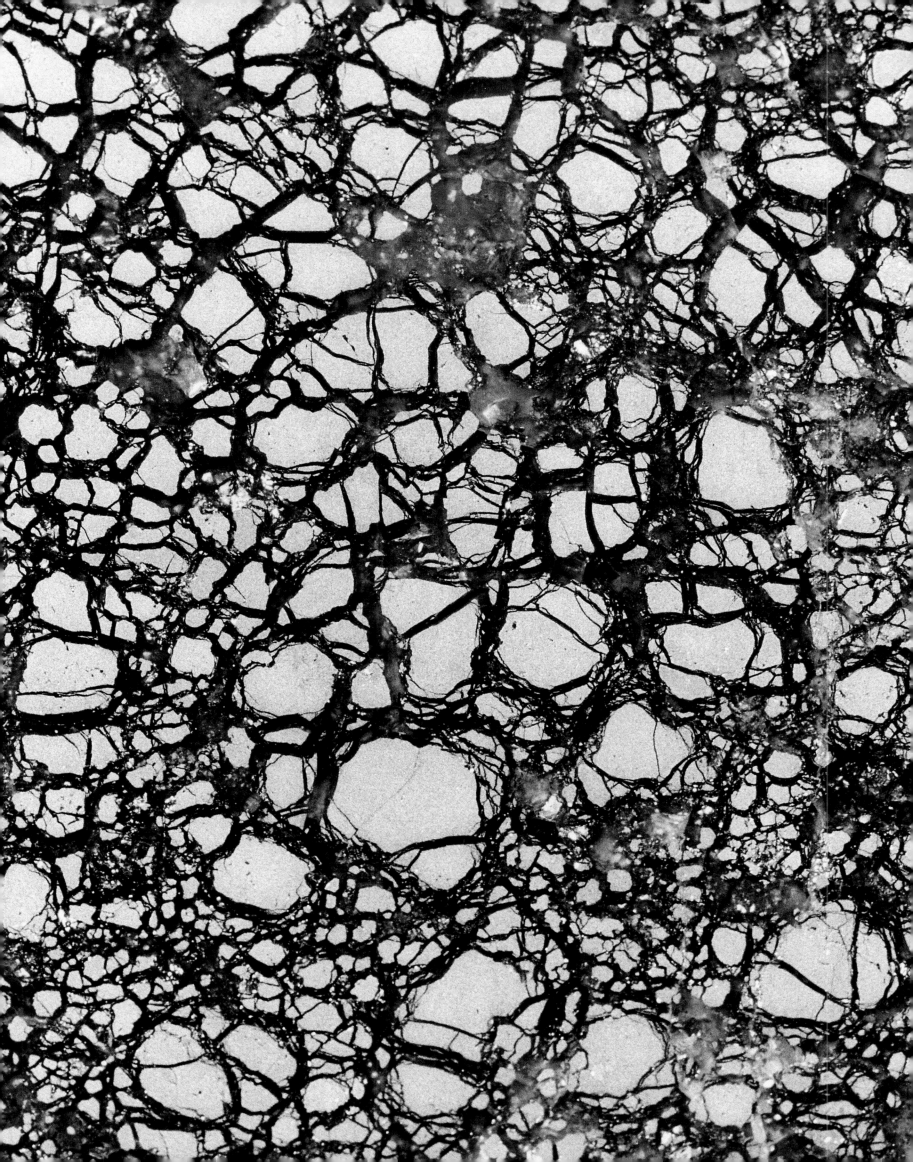

10 *and* 12 *(following pages)* | **MANGANESE DENDRITES** |
SOLNHOFEN, BAVARIA, GERMANY
Although dendrites have nothing to do with plant life, they
often resemble sea anemones, bushes or tall thistles in
the grass.

11 | **EAGLEWOOD LIMESTONE WITH DENDRITES** |
CUSTER CO., SOUTH DAKOTA, USA
An artist's studies of bushes and trees? The word 'dendrite'
comes from the Greek word *dendron*, a tree.

13 | **DENDRITE AGATE** | KAZAKHSTAN
Dendrites can also grow in opaque agate. They have the
appearance of hazily painted bushes in the evening light.

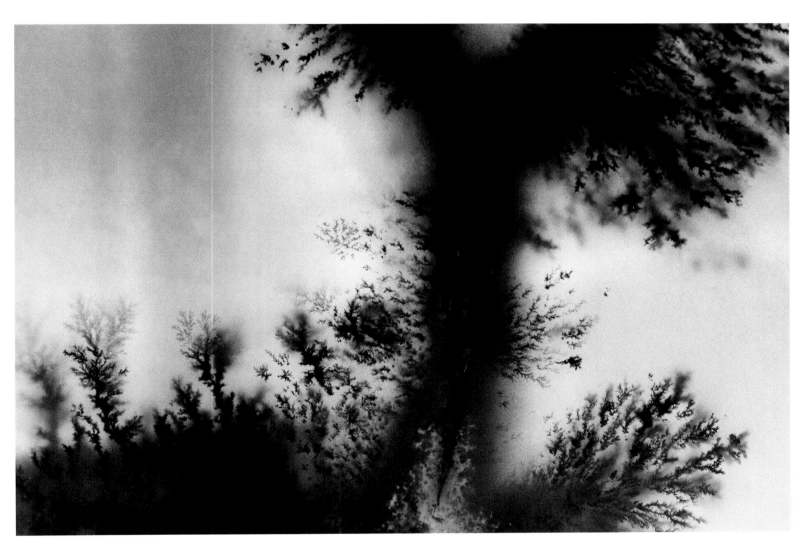

14 | **DENDRITE AGATE** | KAZAKHSTAN
More trees and bushes at sunset.

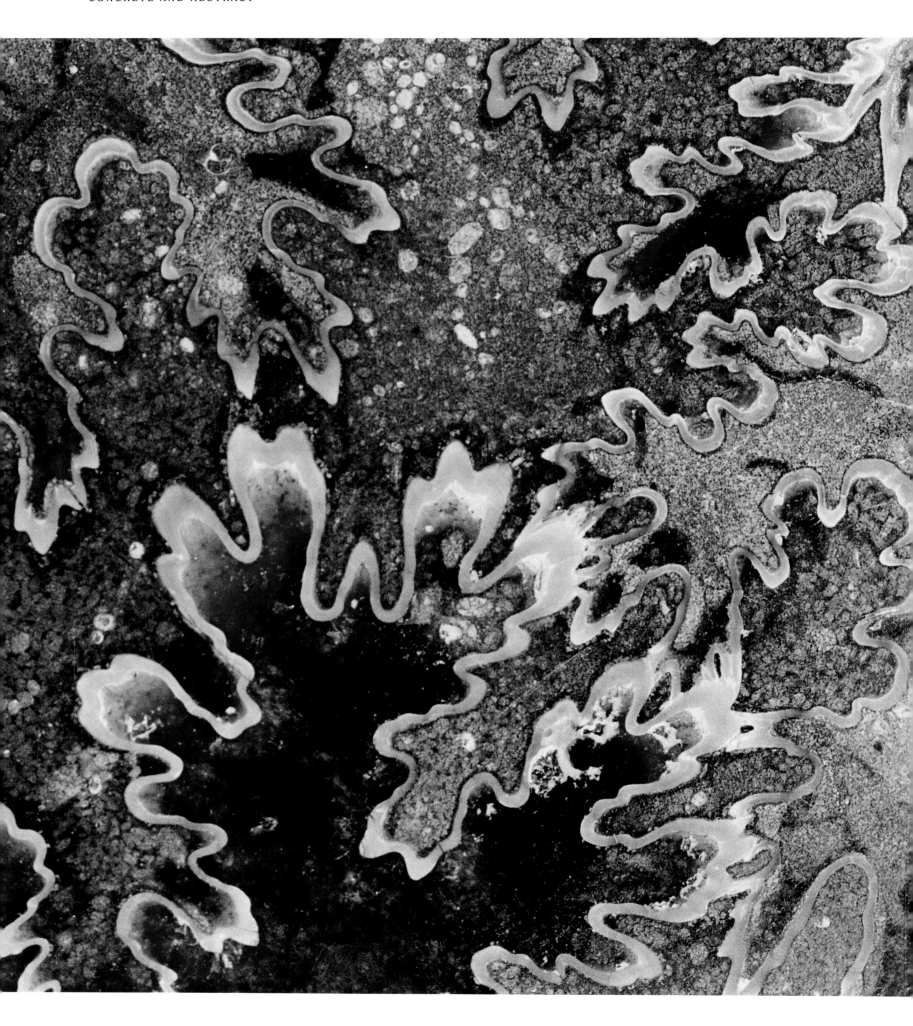

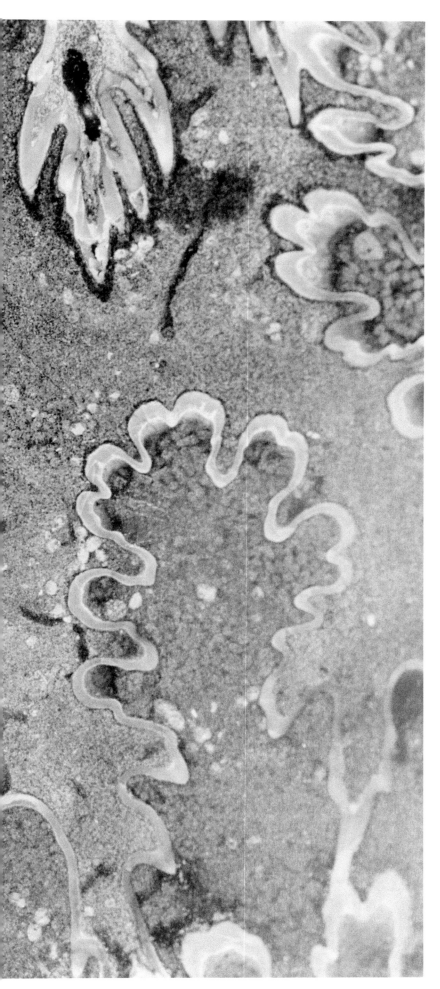

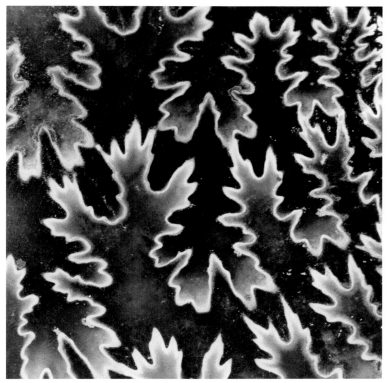

15 *and* 16 | **LOBE LINES OF AN AMMONITE (CHETONICERAS)** | MAHAJUNGA, MADAGASCAR
These fossils from the Middle Cretaceous period, some 100 million years old, show the organs with which the ammonite became fused with its shell. Although of animal origin, this has produced an attractive leaf pattern.

17 | **NAUTILUS** | MADAGASCAR
This creature, petrified some 170 million years ago, was cut
up to make visible its stunningly beautiful system of regular
chambers. Within are the crystals which formed during the
petrifaction of the animal, coloured dark and light brown,
while the outer area has sea-green crystals, which seem to
be heaped up like little jewels.

18 | **AMMONITE** | MORONDARA, MADAGASCAR
This ammonite was petrified some 150 million years ago. The
baroque-looking spiral housing resembles the workings of
old pocket watches.

1 | **CONDOR AGATE** | SAN RAFAEL, PATAGONIA, ARGENTINA
Five images have been created from this stone.
Size of the stone: 16cm x 11.5cm

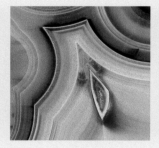
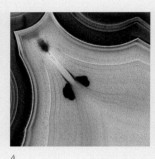

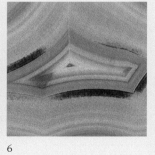

2　　　　　3　　　　　4　　　　　5　　　　　6

A LOOK INTO THE WORKSHOP

These sharp, crystal-clear images of stones from the depths of the Earth might seem to be a matter of course. But much time and a work process of many steps are needed to make possible this view into the structure of the stone. To produce a polished stone, in all cases the stone must first be hewn out of a larger block or from the rock itself. In conventional quarries, whole sections of the mountain are sometimes broken up, and the material thus freed can then be worked upon, and brought to the required form and size. With more valuable material – for example white Carrara marble – the blocks are cut from the rock. They are cut with long steel cables, sometimes set with pieces of diamond, which run over rollers and work their way into the stone over periods of days or weeks. With geodes or almond-shaped agate inclusions this physical quarrying is of course not necessary.

Cut stones are still matt in appearance and have a pattern with irregular grooves, from the cable or the diamond-set cutting disc. As a next step towards the final polished stone, the material is ground, first roughly, then more and more finely, and the last, finest stage is the true polishing, which produces a shining upper surface. It is this final polishing stage that allows us to 'look inside' the stone. If one wants to know whether a stone will reward the lengthy process of polishing, one can moisten it. Then the colours will shine out and one will see – though admittedly not yet very clearly – the patterning of the stone. The film of moisture closes the pores of the raw stone and simulates a smooth surface – an experiment that can be made with any pebble from a stream.

Georg Kern has chosen the most suitable examples from an abundance of stones that have come into his possession over the years, to put under the lens of his camera. His eye, trained by his lifelong experience with the camera, seeks out the best sections in order to produce the most interesting shots, not to mention the most aesthetically attractive.

ONE STONE – MANY IMAGES

The following series of images gives a glimpse into Kern's 'workshop'. The 16cm x 11.5cm Condor Agate from Patagonia, at the southern tip of South America, has produced five highly attractive images alone, to be seen here – and it could produce even more, but these would not satisfy Kern's rigid selection criteria. The most rewarding parts of it (2-5) are the edge and corner areas and of course the great central field (6) with the centre of the geode, which is here completely filled. This magnificent agate is the source of five superb pictures. These images possess a persuasive beauty, with their elegant forms and their wonderfully graduated colours, which nevertheless go so well together. One single cut and polished geode shows in principle all the diversity of agates: the lively play of lines, their precise parallelism, the gradation of the shades of colour and their unbelievably delicate pastel transitions; but also, at the edges, the areas where the colours merge into one another as in a watercolour, and parts with the strong red tones, as in the popular image of agates.

But in this one piece, we also see – as if brought together in a menu – all the formal and geological elements that occur so frequently in this book: almost spherical forms (2), then the elegant lines of symmetry which can become images like the calyx of a flower (4), or the eye-shaped areas (3) in whose centres, on close observation, we can recognize macrocrystalline, clear rock crystals, which have had time to grow and to fill up remaining openings.

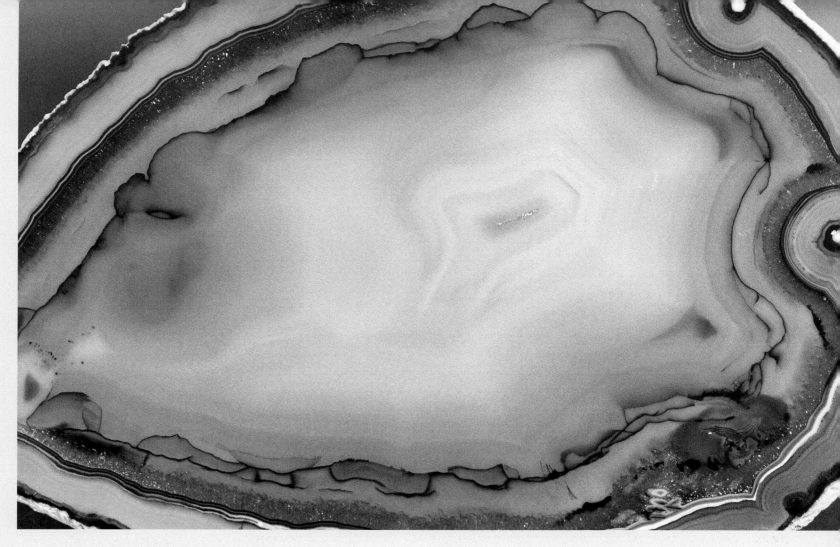

7 | **PANORAMA AGATE** | SOLEDADE, RIO GRANDE
DO SUL, BRAZIL
The images on pages 130, 132, 136, 137, 214, and 215 were
created from this stone.

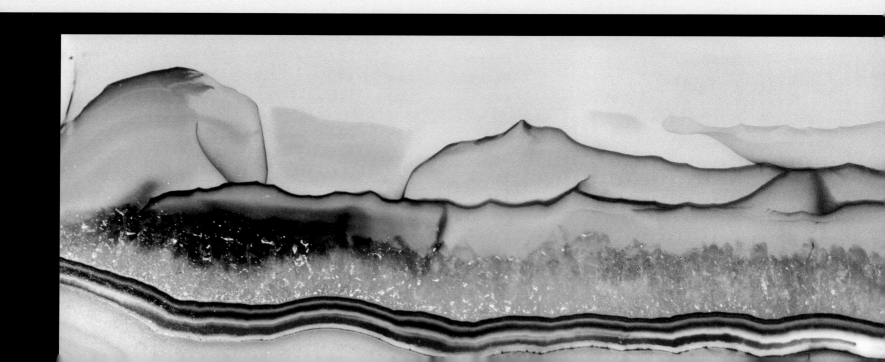

PANORAMA OF THE PANORAMA AGATE

Quite a different picture is presented by the Panorama Agate from Soledade in the Rio Grande do Sul province in Brazil. The image shows the very recognizable agate disc (7), the round-to-oval form of the geode with its raw outer crust. Then, moving inwards, there follow pale yellow bands, closed off by a pale blue line, partly set off in black on both sides. Above this – still moving inwards – a layer of rock crystal has built up, in relatively large crystals, whose surfaces reflect the sunlight as it strikes them, giving it a glittering wreath. There follows another pale yellow microcrystalline layer of agate, followed by a further black line which – for whatever reason – no longer follows a straightforward path, but splits, above all in the lower region of the geode, and develops into a calligraphy which unfortunately

we are no longer able to read. It tells of a very dramatic phase in the history, many millions of years long, of this Brazilian agate. Traumatic events have left behind a drawing of exquisite beauty – a beauty not only of form but of colour. This lively, picturesque region of the agate has a particularly attractive effect, because a very fine microcrystalline mass has formed in the innermost part, in shades of chalcedony blue and almost white, which provides an ideal background for the dramatic 'panorama' images. The delicate pastel tones predominate in the inner areas, but as usual we can again see in the innermost core a few gleaming macrocrystalline crystals, which have finally closed off the inner space of the geode. This splendid example of agate allows not only a number of very fine individual images to be made, but also – more obviously in the case of a Panorama Agate – a kind of panoramic view (see below).

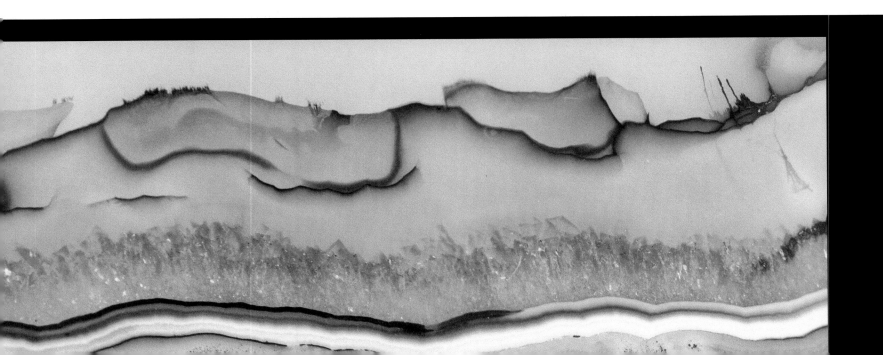

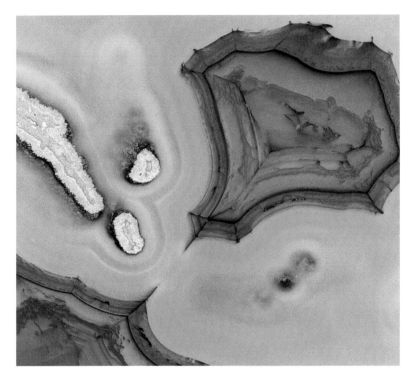

8 | **AGATE** | BRAZIL
In reflected light

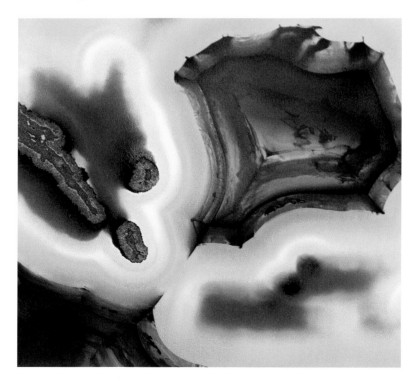

9 | **AGATE** | BRAZIL
In transmitted light

REFLECTED AND TRANSMITTED LIGHT

Without exception, Georg Kern's photographs have been taken in sunlight. Anyone who wants to buy a new item of clothing prefers to take it briefly out of the shop to see it in daylight, because this is the only way of being certain of seeing its genuine colours. The ideal source of light for us is the sun, which in the area where Georg Kern lives, at about 700 metres above sea-level, often shines and is very bright and undimmed.

Generally, thin-layered polished stones are mostly translucent. Our forebears made use of this fact, and in very old buildings we often find windows constructed not with glass, but with alabaster or with a thin, transparent layer of marble. Georg Kern has of course also made use of the translucency of polished stones, above all of agates, and the result is pictures which, in terms not only of colour but of form, have acquired quite a new expressive power. The difference between reflected and transmitted light becomes clear by comparison (8–11). What blazes in friendly bright colours in reflected light, with a few sparkling reflections where macrocrystalline formations or metallic inclusions occur, has a dramatic tension when seen in transmitted light. What was previously bright appears uncanny, menacing or simply, somehow, romantically transfigured. The diaphanous, partly translucent stone allows only a selected part of the sunlight through, only the wavelengths that are not filtered out. The colours acquire a new intensity, such as we see in stained glass in churches, or in colour slides. As beautiful as landscapes, trees or flowers can be when seen against the light, transparent plates of stone can have just as magical and strange an effect in transmitted light. The lifelong experience of our observing eyes tells us that a world is hidden behind the polished stone.

If we gaze at a thin, transparent coloured plate of agate in a striking light, it may, for example, appear blue. If one now turns it against the source of light and looks at it in transmitted light, an astonishing exchange of colours takes place. What appeared blue before is now yellowish-brown. This exchange of colours is known to experts by the term 'pleochromism'. Pleochromism occurs in certain crystals – in our example of agate, in quartz crystals – as a result of the fact that they separate the sunlight into various colours, depending on the direction of its striking. (The phenomenon can be easily observed in the series of pairs of images, 8–11.)

With reflected light, one thinks one is able to penetrate with one's eye into the depths of the semi-transparent material, in a similar way to that in which one can observe water creatures through the glass in an aquarium, or senses, rather than perceives, the contours of trees or houses through fog. One tries to 'see into' the depths, until one has come to the limits of one's visual power and one's eyes feel painful. With transmitted light, on the other hand, the stone and its colours light up as though it were itself the source of light. Many details are covered up by the opaquely diffused light, and remain invisible. But the shining of the stone brings forth an intensity of colour and an unfamiliar atmosphere. Churchmen have made this effect their own with their stained-glass church windows, in order to create a particularly solemn or even obscure mood, and today many night-clubs and restaurants work with similar effects, where the backlit material may be coloured glass, fabric or finely polished wood veneer.

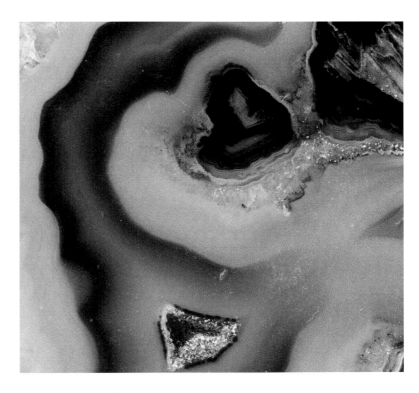

10 | **AGATE** | BRAZIL
In reflected light

11 | **AGATE** | BRAZIL
In transmitted light

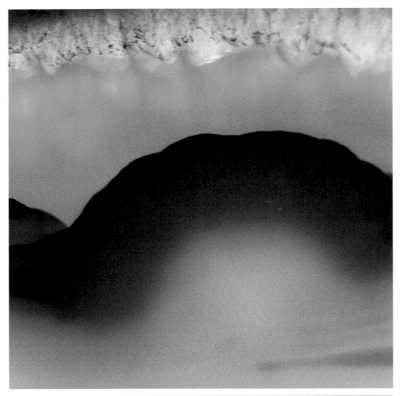

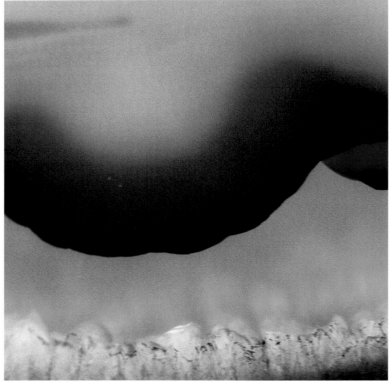

12 *and* 13 | **AGATE** | SOLEDADE, RIO GRANDE DO SUL, BRAZIL

WHAT IS WRONG WITH THIS PICTURE?

Just as we can aim at new effects with light, show new variants and indulge in games, we can also allow our sense of orientation to become deliberately confused. The geodes – which came into being many millions of years ago, were later torn out of their earlier environment by weathering and were often transported like pebbles in rubble and debris – have long had no real 'top' or 'bottom'. They have been turned round perhaps thousands of times and consist of periphery and centre, but further coordinates are not defined. The sphere knows neither front nor back, left or right, top or bottom.

But we humans live in a world defined by gravity. We stand on the ground, the plumb-line gives us our vertical line, the water level defines the horizontal. Consciously or subconsciously, we subordinate everything we perceive and observe to these natural living conditions of ours. We need these coordinates to find our way in life and the world, and our sense of balance does not like it at all if the spatial structure in which we find ourselves is taken out of our control. When, on a rough sea, the horizon of the sea rises and falls outside the windows of a ship's restaurant, many people quickly lose their appetite

It is quite understandable, therefore, that we always seek to define a 'top' and a 'bottom'. With sections of polished stones fixed in photographic images, to be hung on a wall or printed in a book, it is necessary to choose a 'top' and a 'bottom'. With the direction of the camera, with its predetermined rectangular form, Georg Kern, whether arbitrarily, deliberately, instinctively or simply with the trained eye of a photographer, creates a horizon, an invisible network of coordinates in 'his' stones. This too is to some extent a 'creative' act: the stones – whose very complex physical and chemical origins are explained elsewhere in this book – are taken out of their physical conditions and transferred to the system of our physical nature, which is characterized by gravitation. With many of Georg Kern's photographs it is the task of the trained eye to determine the correct detail and the 'correct' location of the photograph. With others – above all, of course, those that remind us of landscapes – no questions are posed in this respect. We automatically 'read' the image in the way we have been used to do all our lives. The landscape lies below, the 'sky' curves above.

Various agates with forms reminiscent of landscape can however confuse and test our inherent sense of orientation. Some examples here show how the images can be turned through 180 degrees so that another – confusingly, just as convincing – landscape is to be seen: dark mountains against a light-coloured sky (15, below) or a light-coloured hilly landscape against a dark, overcast sky (14, above). Of course this is no more than a game played with our senses, with our acquired manner of interpreting the impressions we receive, as we have been used to do from experience. But it is a delightful game, which shows us how Georg Kern's photographs need to be understood: as an invitation to let the beauty hidden in the stones, made visible by means of cutting, grinding and polishing, and held fast by the camera, work on us and excite our imagination.

14 *and* 15 | **AGATE** | SOLEDADE, RIO GRANDE DO SUL, BRAZIL

16 | **AGATE ALMOND** | MASHATU, BOTSWANA, AFRICA
This image shows both halves of the opened geode.

THE GEODES AND THEIR PORTRAITIST

An agate almond or geode (16) looks from the outside not very different from any large pebble. Admittedly, the surface is not usually so heavily ground by debris and sand, but rather looks weathered. As soon as it has been cut and polished a little, what is hidden within it can be seen. Then the great 'open sesame' moment arrives, when the geode is bisected and both halves are polished. As with wood veneer or marble plates, the result is two practically symmetrical, almost identical surfaces. They are really never precisely symmetrical, for the diamond-set cutting disc damages the grown stone – a thin layer of material is always lost in the cutting and polishing process.

Over the years, Georg Kern has put his collection into perfect order. He knows exactly where to look for a particular material. From the multiplicity of objects he chooses a suitable one, observes the quality and finally examines the piece under the stereomicroscope. In his garden, in full sunlight, the qualities of the cut stone can be seen in both reflected and transmitted light; time to prepare the camera and use the viewfinder to determine the ideal image. And so starts a highly exciting hunt for ever more beautiful and exciting images.

AGATES

About half of the images collected in this book show agates. This variety of quartz comes from a family of minerals marked by an immense variety. Let us take a closer look at the 'agates'.

HOW DOES ONE RECOGNIZE AGATES?

Agates are a microcrystalline variety of quartz and are defined as banded chalcedony, often coloured in layers by iron-containing pigments (see Glossary).

The banding is the most striking characteristic of agates. The mostly parallel lines remind one of the annual rings of trees. The banding of agates has very varied manifestations; it can be parallel or concentric (spherical). There are monochrome agates, whose banding is visible only through the finest nuances of colour, and polychrome agates with strongly marked banding, for example in white, black and red. In one piece of agate, the most diverse variations may appear in different places.

Most agates have sharply drawn banding, but there are others with blurred, indefinite lines. According to the angle at which the stone is cut, the layers are separated in different ways, resulting in different images. With certain agates, images of clouds, waves, or plants appear – images that can be traced back to the varied structural nature of the agate.

With some agates the image is additionally characterized by coarse crystalline quartz. This crystal-shaped quartz may be entirely enclosed within the agate, but separate fragments of quartz may also appear. Such agates give us pleasure through their sheen and the play of colours evoked by the refraction of light on the edges of the grain of individual quartz crystals.

The cause of the light refraction, however, may also be various enclosed foreign minerals. There are agates whose appearance is determined to a great extent by enclosed foreign material, that is through sheaf-shaped, plant-like, but also spherical crystal aggregate or individual needles of crystal. These formations can also fill the entire cavity. If this happens, then the chalcedony substance penetrating the foreign material may be unable to form any visible structures.

The agate is a hard stone, which lends itself well to being treated by cutting, grinding and polishing with diamond tools. Only through this process does the originally inconspicuous lump of agate reveal the full beauty of its colours and forms.

The essential part – the basic character – of the agate lies not in the microscopic or the radiological, but in the area visible to the naked eye. This visible realm is also the basis of a systematics of agates.

One can also compare the structure of the agate with that of wood. The banding corresponds to the annual rings of wood, while the fibrous nature of wood corresponds to the radiality of the agate. The path of the bands, which can take any degree of curve from a straight line to a circle, depends on external circumstances. Often the walls of the cavity into which agate has been precipitated are copied by the form and direction of the bands.

The question of the origin of the agate formation, with its colours and the varying degree of transparency of the individual bands of agate, leads us deep into mineralogy.

On the basis of examinations under the microscope, it can be stated that chalcedony, the basic substance of agate, is in terms of crystallography a finely crystallized fibrous quartz. In the same way, we recognize only from laboratory experiments that it consists chemically of silicic acid (silicium dioxide). Further chemical, optical, radiographic and crystallographic research supplies the answers to further questions. Thick-fibred layers of chalcedony are opaque and white; with increased density of the individual crystal fibres the chalcedony becomes transparent. The various colours of chalcedony are created by the layering of finely distributed mineral colour pigments in the gaps in the crystal.

But all scientific findings are not enough to describe adequately the qualities of agate, which is defined graphically as chalcedony. The appearance of agate is composed of elements which we can understand through scientific methods, but its astonishing beauty lies in the order and harmony of the whole, in the repetition, in the lively movement of its markings, in its wealth of contrasts, in the relationships and transitions of the elements. Our primary, that is integrated, experience of the agate, of stone and nature in general, is not a scientific one, but a sensual and aesthetic one.

Contact with images of agate not only makes one curious about the history of the origin of agates and the causes of their colours, their contrasts and transitions, but also raises the question of what these images have to say to us and what impressions and feelings they release in the observer.

WHERE ARE AGATES TO BE FOUND?

Agates are found in many parts of the world – above all in places where volcanism has been a feature of the Earth's history. An example is the classic, historic site of Idar-Oberstein in Germany. At the end of the Palaeozoic era (250 to 300 million years ago), in Perm, Russia, extensive volcanic activity led to the formation of agate deposits.

The process started when a spreading stream of lava cooled down. This happens most rapidly at the upper and lower sides. In these areas, the gases contained in the hot lava first separated from the magma, and gas bubbles formed in the smaller and larger cavities in the viscous mass. The inner part of the stream of lava was hotter and therefore more fluid. Here, the gas bubbles moved upwards and combined with others, so that larger cavities were created. Through the movement of the lava stream, the cavities were elongated in the direction of its flow. These many small and large cavities are the basic precondition for the later formation of agates.

These cavities are called geodes. If they are entirely filled with agate, quartz or other minerals, they are called almonds. If the filling is incomplete, so that some of the cavity remains, the geode is called a druse.

Agates are secondary cavity fillings in vulcanites: quartz-containing material that has later penetrated the cavities and gradually filled them up. The agates themselves are therefore not volcanic products.

WHERE DOES THE FILLING COME FROM? AT WHAT POINT IN TIME DID IT COME INTO BEING?

Some 30-50 million years after the formation of lava streams, in the Idar-Oberstein area, there followed a so-called post-volcanic hydrothermal phase; that is, long after the volcanic activity, hot, watery suspensions began to circulate in the stones. In time, beginning at the rims of the cavities, new microcrystalline layers began to form. This is when the silicium dioxide (SiO_2) minerals (quartz and its variants) form, which in succession fill the cavities: the agate comes into being.

In a later phase, over long geological periods, the volcanic stones become weathered. First, the softer components of the stone formations begin to weather. The harder parts – the geodes with the hard quartz or agate – are preserved as lumps or balls, and are found in the debris of rivers, or as stones, which can be found on the surface of the earth in former volcanic areas. The geodes can also be removed by mining the volcanic area.

Agates are also found within Europe in the Czech Republic and in Italy (Sicily). Outside Europe, the best and most productive agate deposit sites are found, first of all, in Brazil, then in Argentina, in North America and in Mexico. In Africa, agates are found in Madagascar, Botswana, Zimbabwe and Morocco. In Asia, Indonesia and India supply fine agates, as do Borneo and Mongolia. Good agates are also found in Australia. This list does not claim to be comprehensive.

HOW EXACTLY WERE AGATES CREATED?

Agate has been known for millennia, and is to be found worldwide in innumerable places, mined and worked by the ton, and studied by many scientists in varied fields. To date there is no generally accepted theory about the origin of agates, which may seem surprising.

None of the previous agate theories could really explain their origin, but Professor Michael Landmesser of the University of Mainz, who has for years been at the forefront of research into the origin of agate, has developed a new idea. With a probability verging on certainty, agates are former colloidal systems. Such systems are exceedingly resistant to scientific access. Colloid suspensions with almost the same qualities can behave in completely different ways. A difficult basic question is: how could the substance of agates, mainly silicium dioxide (SiO_2), accumulate in a stone cavity to form compact, hard bodies?

In a phase of intensive research into agate over a period of some 200 years, no really plausible mechanism has been found. Research into agate has positively worked itself to death over this basic problem. Many famous mineralogists have in fact given up the attempt to answer this question, because the effective SiO_2 accumulation mechanism by means of watery suspensions, sought for so long but in vain, after mature consideration did not, after all, seem possible.

HOW AND IN WHAT FORM DID THE AGATE GET INTO THE CAVITY?

This is the primary and decisive question on the agate problem. Since larger fractures or fissures leading to the agate almonds, in which watery suspensions can freely circulate, are often absent in stone, one must assume that the SiO_2 of the agates was normally not transported to the almonds by fluid suspensions, but through diffusion, above all a diffusion of the dissolved molecule $Si(OH)_4$.

This process takes place at a later stage than the cooling of the volcanic stone, probably often not until it has been covered with sediments or further volcanic stone, but certainly not before watery suspensions have become distributed in the fine capillaries of the vulcanite, that is when the vulcanite has been permeated by a fine net of porous suspension.

By diffusion, it is meant the movement of dissolved substances, without the porous suspension itself being moved. The transportation of SiO_2 thus takes place within more or less immobile porous suspensions, which moisten the finest pores in the secondary stones and at the same time entirely fill the great cavities, in which the agates are formed. In these, the SiO_2 is then precipitated in the form of bands. An important development in recent research into agate has been that it has become possible to clarify the physical and chemical bases and driving forces in this process of diffusion and accumulation. Maturing SiO_2 bodies 'attract' the dissolved SiO_2 from its environment and build it into themselves. Tiny micropores in the maturing agate are thus filled with completing SiO_2.

The agate, at first soft and gelatinous, thus becomes ever richer in SiO2 and harder. Deformations in agate can only be explained if one assumes – at the start of the process of formation of agate – malleable, gelatinous, but already banded SiO2 precipitations on the cavity walls.

So the agate was not directly precipitated in the hard, dense form in which it is found at the conclusion of the entire process.

The morphology of agates seems at first glance not to follow any simple, generally valid rule. It is all the more amazing, therefore, that the originally individual agate does then nevertheless manifest an almost perfect inner order, the most outstanding aspect of which is its often extraordinarily regular rhythmic banding. This curious relationship of tension between the apparent chaos of forms of the many agates and the perfect inner order in each individual agate is probably one of the reasons for the power to fascinate, but also the enigmatic nature of the natural phenomenon that is the agate. This is what makes it so exciting!

CAN ONE DRAW CONCLUSIONS ABOUT ITS ORIGIN FROM THE IMAGE OFFERED BY AN AGATE THAT HAS BEEN CUT OPEN?

Agate structures reveal themselves as positive keys to the understanding of their origins. Many details of the story of their formation are documented in them.

Normal banding in agates by no means slavishly follows the form of the cavity. Rather, one finds on the cavity walls morphologically independent, semi-spherical, banded SiO2-aggregates: banded spheroliths. If such spheroliths grow together, the result is a joint banding pattern. Sharp corners sometimes occur where spheroliths have made contact with each other, or between the features of spheroliths where they inhibit each other in their further development.

HOW SHOULD WE IMAGINE THE BEGINNING OF THE PROCESS OF AGATE FORMATION?

At the beginning of the process we have a cavity entirely filled with hot porous suspension, but otherwise empty, which is linked with its environment by means of very fine capillaries filled with suspension.

By these means, various dissolved substances – for example SiO2 – can become diffused in the cavity. Within the cavity, because of the high concentration of SiO2, colloid particles of SiO2 will form – very fine, amorphous particles, which float in the suspension and also remain floating through Brownian motion. However, from individual points on the cavity wall they can combine into gelatinous, semi-spherical, banded aggregates.

These are the predecessors of the later, hard chalcedony spheroliths. That they must once have been soft can be recognized in certain agates from the deformed spheroliths.

HOW CAN AN EVEN HORIZONTAL PARALLEL BANDING DEVELOP IN THE DYNAMIC AGATE SYSTEM?

Through the power of gravity, small particles sink down in the suspension and form horizontal, unestablished predecessors of the so-called Uruguay banding.

Iron-containing pigments may already have become embedded at the point of settling of the individual gelatinous layers, or enter later through the somewhat porous chalcedony. In this way, colouring substances may selectively – in bands – get into the agate. Colouring of this kind by bands is possible at an even earlier stage, in which the developing agate has not yet matured into the hard, dense chalcedony.

HOW DOES THE 'MOSS' GET INTO THE AGATE?

Sometimes tubular, usually curved, often branched formations traverse the agate with rounded cross-sections. Such agates have long been referred to as 'moss agates'. Most moss agate tubes are usually crystals of chlorite, growing in the colloidal system (sol) of the developing agate.

HOW LONG DOES A SINGLE AGATE TAKE TO DEVELOP?

The collection of completing SiO_2 in the micropores of maturing SiO_2 bodies is a process which can take place over geological periods, and in certain documented cases has extended over millions of years.

The formation of siliceous wood (petrified wood) must also have taken place over many millions of years. The possible range of duration of the maturing and accumulation processes of SiO_2 is however very great, depending on the temperature and on chemical parameters. In contact with relatively SiO_2-rich suspensions, at room temperature over experimentally comprehensible periods of time, quartz does not crystallize at all!

So a minimum period of decades, if not centuries, is to be assumed for the development of agates. The decisive processes at any rate take place too slowly to be directly followed in the laboratory under conditions close to those of nature.

Agates can appear not only as cavity fillings in amber, but also in many other low-thermal formations, such as cavity fillings in sedimental stones or various fossils. In the formation of flint or petrified wood a similar accumulation process of SiO_2 appears, functioning at low temperatures (below 200°C).

HOW OLD ARE AGATES?

As already mentioned above, the agates from the Idar-Oberstein area in Germany, for example, came into being more than 200 million years ago. In general it may be said that agates are always millions of years old. They were formed in all geological eras by volcanic activity. The condition for this was that the preconditions over very long periods of time remained fairly constant: the presence of (300–400°C) hot suspensions supersaturated with SiO_2, with constant composition under heightened pressure.

Only through the combination of fortunate geological conditions could agates come into being. According to ways in which these conditions varied somewhat, but remained constant at a particular location, forms of agate developed which were typical of that location. An agate expert can therefore easily assign particular agates to certain sites where they originated.

Dr Georg Kern

Bibliography:

Naturhistorisches Museum Basel (ed.)/Arnoth Josef, *Achate: Bilder im Stein*, Buchverlag Basler Zeitung, Basel 1986

'Achat, der Edelstein, aus dem Idar-Oberstein entstanden ist', in *Extra-Lapis* no.19, Christian Weise-Verlag, Munich 2000

GLOSSARY

AGATE
The name is of Greek origin. The stone was named after the first location where it was found, by the river Achates in Sicily.

The agate is a banded chalcedony (SiO_2), often coloured in layers by iron-containing pigments, that is, a quartz. It is mostly found as a filling in bubble cavities in vulcanites. The banding may be parallel or concentric (spherical). With the agate almond, the whole of the cavity is filled with agate. In the case of the agate geode, quartz crystals have formed in a remaining cavity.

Agate and quartz have the same chemical formula, SiO_2, and the same crystal structure. Rock crystal and agate are two varieties of quartz and only differ as to the size of crystal – monocrystal on the one hand, microcrystal on the other.
Monocrystals (macrocrystalline): for example, rock crystal, amethyst, cairngorm, etc.
Microcrystals: for example, jasper
Cryptocrystals: for example, chalcedony, agate

ALMOND
The almond is a geode which is entirely filled with minerals (such as agate and/or quartz).

AMMONITE
Named after the Greek god Ammon, who was represented with ram's horns. Ammonites are extinct, fossilized cephalopods; that is, their spiral-shaped petrified shells, also called Ammon's horn. Ammonites are index fossils, which lived from the Silurian to the end of the Cretaceous period. They were swimming sea inhabitants. The present-day nautilus is a descendant of the ammonites.

ARAUCARIA
Location: southern America, Australia, Oceania.
Conifer trees up to 60 metres high, with needles or overlapping leaves, bearing spherical cones with unwinged seeds.

Pictured on page 35 is a section through a petrified (fossil) cone from an Araucaria mirabilis of the Jura era, 100–140 million years old, from Cerro Cuadrado, Patagonia, Argentina.

AZURITE
Blue azurite, like green malachite, is a copper carbonate. Both occur in oxidation areas of copper deposit sites.

BRECCIA
A breccia is composed of angular debris of stone and minerals, secured by a binding substance such as chalk. Round pebbles that are bound together again are known by the German term *Nagelfluh*.

CALCITE
The name comes from the Latin *calx*, chalk. The chemical formula is $CaCO_3$, calcium carbonate. A very common mineral.

CHALCEDONY
Named after the ancient Greek city of Chalcedon at the entrance to the Bosphorus. Chalcedony is a cryptocrystalline quartz aggregate and the generic term for all varieties of colour and form:
Agate: banded chalcedony
Chrysoprase: green chalcedony from nickel silicate deposits
Carneol: red chalcedony
Sard: brown chalcedony
Onyx: black chalcedony

CHRYSOCOLLA
Chrysocolla is a green aqueous copper silicate, which results from the oxidation of copper ores.

COLLOID, COLLOIDS
(From Greek *kolla*, glue.)
The colloidal condition of a substance is identified by the size of its particles. This is generally 0.3 to 1μm, that is, less than a thousandth of a millimetre. In a colloid suspension, the contents are not – as with a genuine 'suspension' – so widely spread out that individual molecules or atoms move around within it. Rather, thousands of molecules have become concentrated into colloidal particles. One cannot see them with the naked eye, but one can see the optical phenomena they cause, such as light scattering. Some materials are capable to a special degree of the formation of colloids, such as glue (*kolla*), protein and silicic acid. A colloid 'suspension' is called a sol. Further concentration and subsequent flocculation produces gels.

CRAZY LACE AGATE
The name alone reveals a great deal about this spectacular stone. This form of agate from the Santa Rita mine in the Sierra Santa Lucia, Chihuahua province, in Mexico, is a pseudomorphosis of agate after calcite. Its forms are very characteristic, of great structural diversity (so-called fortification agate forms), and it is often very colourful.

DRUSE
Druse is the name given to a geode in which crystals have formed, which project into the remaining cavity.

FLUORITE
The chemical composition of fluorite is CaF_2. It is a common mineral and can be either colourless or purple, blue, yellow or green.

GEL
Many materials are capable of forming colloids. Through the concentration of small colloidal particles in fluids, voluminous precipitations are formed, so-called gels.

But a colloidal suspension can also become gelatinous as a whole, for example bone glue or fruit juice. Jellies can alter their volume through shrinkage or swelling.

A solidified gel is not crystalline. However, originally gelatinous materials may later enter a crystalline state. This is known, for example, with agate and chalcedony.

A colloidal suspension is called a sol. Further concentration or flocculation of the small particles results in gels.

GLOSSARY

GEODE
A cavity (bubble cavity), such as quartz, usually spherical, lined with crystals, found in most rounded vulcanites.

HAWK'S EYE
Location: South Africa, Australia.
Like the Tiger's Eye, a Hawk's Eye is a quartz with inclusions of weathered crocidolite (amphibole asbestos). Often colourful.

HELIOTROPE
Heliotrope is a green-coloured, microcrystalline quartz with embedded red iron pigments, for this reason it is also known as bloodstone.

IRON NICKEL METEORITE
The iron nickel meteorite is an extra-terrestrial solid that has fallen to the earth's surface through the terrestrial atmosphere. Some 5 per cent of all meteorites are iron nickel meteorites, with a nickel content of 5–12 per cent. Typical are the Widmannstätten patterns on the cut and polished surface of the piece of meteorite.

JASPER
Jasper is a microcrystalline, opaque quartz aggregate, often brightly coloured from other embedded minerals (such as iron pigments).

LAGUNA AGATE
Location: Laguna region at Villa Ahumada, Chihuahua, Mexico.
Intensively banded, often multicoloured, agate.

LANDSCAPE MARBLE (*Pietra paesina*)
Location: east of Florence, Tuscany (Italy). Age: c. 140 million years. Landscape marbles were formed in the Lower Cretaceous geological period. This is a mixed stone formed under the sea, fine-grained and sedimentary, with a high calcium content and consisting of up to 15 per cent clay minerals.

Landscape marble is petrographically a calcium marl, not marble. The brown, yellow ochre and red colour of earth comes predominantly from iron mixtures. Iron is the fourth most common element and the most common heavy metal in the Earth's crust, and usually occurs only in a chemical combination. Apart from iron mixtures, manganese oxide, which otherwise often forms dendrites, also plays a part in the formation of landscape marble.

Paesina was already known to the ancient Romans. Pietra paesina is a simple limestone, which has aroused the interest and the imagination of humans over the centuries, and continues to do so. It is a little piece of the Earth's crust from the primeval oceans, in which imaginary and real landscapes are represented and united.

It is a fortunate cut through the stone that finally determines whether we have in front of us a landscape or only a confused, indefinable pattern.

LANDSCAPE SANDSTONE (KANAB GOLDEN STONE)
Location: Kanab, in southern Utah, USA.
This sandstone was formed in the Trias (Mesozoic) period, 210–220 million years ago, as river deposit and was transported by wind. Sandstone consists of more than 85 per cent hardened quartz grains, with a grain size of 0.02 to 3mm. Iron oxides and iron hydroxides, limonite and haematite (reddish-brown), as well as cilicic acid, serve as binders.

The Kanab Golden Stone patterns are gentler and more flowing than those of the Paesina. Tectonic influences hardly play any part. The main cause of the patterns in sandstone are diffusion and colloid chemical precipitation processes.

LOBE LINES OF AN AMMONITE
Attachment traces of the dividing walls on the inner surface of the ammonite shell. Often characteristically lobed.

MALACHITE
Green malachite, like blue azurite, is a copper carbonate. Both occur in oxidation areas of copper deposit sites.

MANGANESE DENDRITES
Location: In stone fissures (for example, in the Jura limestone of the Solnhofen plates from Bavaria). Manganese dendrites are crystallized, black or brown blends of iron and manganese in the form of moss-like branches. These are not petrified plant forms.

NAUTILUS
The nautilus is the petrified shell of a fossil cephalopod, some 160 million years old, from the large family of the ammonites. A nautilus still living today in tropical oceans is a descendant of this otherwise extinct, but formerly widespread family. The nautilus inhabits the last, largest chamber in his spiral, many-chambered calcium shell.

OPAL
Opals are an aqueous variety of cilicic acid (quartz), originating from gelatinous polysilicic acids (SiO_2). Opals consist of tiny, regular and densely packed balls, which separate the incoming light into the colours of the spectrum (when it is called 'noble opal').

PIETERSITE
Location: Outjo, Namibia.
This is a Ruin Hawk's Eye (comparable to a Ruin Agate).

PYRITE
Called iron pyrites, or sometimes 'cat's gold' because of its golden colour. Chemical formula: FeS_2, iron sulphide. Often found as filling material for fossils.

RHYOLITH
Is a mostly light-coloured vulcanite, rich in quartz. A rhyolith which is old in relation to the Earth's history is often also called quartz porphyry.

RUIN AGATE
Ruin Agates are individual agate fragments (often resulting from tectonic events), that are cemented together with agate substance.

RUTILE QUARTZ
Is a quartz (SiO_2) with embedded, often golden-coloured rutile needles (rutile TiO_2).

SEPTARIUM
A septarium is a bulbous concretion in marly clay, often with crystallizations of calcite and star-shaped fissures.

SILICIFIED WOOD
Silicified wood consists of fossilized woods replaced by hardened silicic acid; that is, the wood pores were filled with SiO_2 suspensions while the structure of the wood was retained.

THUNDER EGG
Thunder egg is the name given to agate almonds weathered out of volcanic lava.

TIGER'S EYE
Location: South Africa, Australia.
A Tiger's Eye, like the Hawk's Eye, is a quartz with inclusions of weathered crocidolite (amphibole asbestos). Often colourful.

TIGER IRON
Location: Australia
Tiger Irons are composed of Tiger's Eye, red jasper and haematite.

URUGUAY AGATE
Uruguay Agate has a horizontally running, straight-lined banding and in the course of its formation oriented itself according to gravity (sediment).

VARISCITE
Location: Fairfield, Utah, USA.
Variscite is a green aluminium phosphate.

VERDE D'ARNO
Location: Florence, Tuscany, Italy.
Verde d'Arno is a green and yellowish-white limestone breccia (marble) with geometric markings.

Dr Georg Kern